SIMPLIFIED
CARPENTRY ESTIMATING

SIMPLIFIED
CARPENTRY ESTIMATING

by

J. DOUGLAS WILSON

Formerly Curriculum Supervisor
Trade and Industrial Education,
City Schools, Los Angeles, California

AND

CLELL M. ROGERS

Formerly Mathematics Instructor
City Schools, Los Angeles, California

FIFTH EDITION

SIMMONS-BOARDMAN PUBLISHING CORPORATION
NEW YORK

Printed in the U. S. A.

FOREWORD

THE PROBLEM of "taking-off" a bill of materials required for the construction of a house is a very important one. Many skilled carpenters are often required to do this work. This book is written to make it possible for them to learn the rules and methods of estimating so they can make accurate building material lists.

The constructional order of quantity survey is used. Each item is taken off from the plan in practically the same order as a building is constructed, beginning with foundation materials, then framing lumber, next exterior finish and lastly interior finish.

When used as a text, each student should also be furnished with a set of residential blueprints and a copy of the check-up measurement sheet on page 5, which is particularly valuable for the beginner. It will then not be difficult to apply the estimating rules for different materials to be listed, reading the plans for all necessary measurements.

Evening school experience using this material when teaching estimating classes has evidenced much interest by many carpenters in the subject of carpentry estimating. We hope skilled craftsmen will find it of profit and interest and that it will be an incentive for carpentry apprentices to study and progress in their trade.

J. DOUGLAS WILSON
CLELL M. ROGERS

PREFACE TO THE FIFTH EDITION

Use of this book as a basic text in Carpentry courses necessitated slight alterations and corrections and the addition of a chapter for a Fifth Edition. The Contents Page has been amplified to show the topical divisions of each chapter.

Because of the book's popularity among master carpenters and contractors the new Chapter XIII, *How to Plan a House,* was added. House contractors will find this a helpful procedure guide in connection with furnishing sound advice to prospective home builders. The practical short cut methods described and the check list have been particularly useful to estimators. Lumber dealers refer to the book for the kind of information they are frequently called on to furnish their customers.

Much of the main text correlates with lessons in the Carpentry curriculum of the State of California. Chapter XII originally was a lesson in the Third Year Carpentry Course published by the California State Department of Education. Thanks is extended the Department for permission to reproduce this material. For permission to reproduce illustrations used in this chapter thanks are extended to the Delmar Publishers, Inc., of Albany, New York.

J. Douglas Wilson
Clell M. Rogers

Los Angeles, Calif.
January, 1950

Reprinted 1954

CONTENTS

CHAPTER   PAGE

I   ESTIMATING FUNDAMENTALS 1

Estimating division—*Foundation, Framing, Exterior Finish, Hardware* — Preliminary Steps — Measurement **Check-up** Sheet—Materials to be Estimated—Estimating **Practices for** Lumber—Fractional Measurements—Plan Symbols—**Plan** Indications — Specifications — Abbreviations — Check-up Procedure.

II   FOUNDATION MATERIALS 13

Concrete Form Unit—Concrete Material Unit—Brick Unit —Concrete Block Unit.

III   FRAMING 29

Underpinning Unit — Floor Unit — Wall Unit: *Western Framing, Balloon Framing*—Ceiling Unit — Roof Unit — Stair Unit.

IV   EXTERIOR FINISH 75

Frame Unit—Wall Unit—Cornice Unit: *Open Cornice, Box Cornice—Roofing Unit.*

V   INTERIOR FINISH 105

Window, Sash, Door and Shutter Unit—Inside Trim Unit— Cabinet Unit—Flooring Unit.

VI   HARDWARE 127

Rough Hardware Unit—Finish Hardware Unit.

VII   BUILDING INFORMATION AND TABLES 144

Building Guide — Lumber — Millwork — Hardware — Ordering Information—Purchasing Unit—Board Foot Constants — Perimeters — Concrete Footings — Concrete Piers — Window Frames — Door Frames — Door and Window Areas — Sash Weights — Nail Sizes and Quantities.

VIII   ESTIMATING SHORT CUTS 177

Framing Lumber — Finish Lumber — Estimator's Checking
List.

IX   LABOR HOURS PER UNIT OF WORK 226

Framing — Exterior Finish — Interior Finish.

X   CARPENTRY MENSURATION 234

Perimeters — Hypotenuse Lengths — Area Rules — Equal
Pitch Roof Areas — Unequal Pitch Roof Areas — Gable
Areas — Volume.

XI   MATHEMATICAL REFERENCE TABLES.. 252

Parts-of-a-Foot Conversion — Decimal Equivalents — Lum-
ber Reckoner — Mensuration — Linear — Surveyor's Long
Measure — Square Measure — Surveyor's Square Measure—
Cubic-Avoirdupois — Liquid — Dry — Circular — Time —
Counting — Metric — Conversion of Weights and Measures
— Common Equivalents — Squares and Square Roots.

XII   STAIR ESTIMATING 264

Construction — Types — Estimating Procedure — Framing
Unit — Finish Unit.

XIII   HOW TO PLAN A HOUSE 279

Your Budget — How to Finance — How to Select Technical
Services — How to Plan a House — Contract Documents
and Requirements — Protection Services Provided — Budget Items.

INDEX 295

CHAPTER I

ESTIMATING FUNDAMENTALS

THERE ARE SEVERAL well defined steps by which the ambitious carpenter may climb and progress in his trade. Naturally as his tool skill increases he becomes more valuable to his employer. Fully as important, the acquiring of technical knowledge pertaining to carpentry will also increase his value as a skilled craftsman. And increased skill usually means more pay.

One very important ability to acquire is that of knowing how to take off a bill of materials. A building cannot be constructed unless someone makes an itemized list of the different materials required, such as framing and finishing lumber, hardware, doors, windows, cement, sand, rock, and a hundred other items. Each of these must be carefully figured to find out the correct quantity or number of pieces and their sizes, lengths, and other information needed to describe them.

An estimator should be thoroughly familiar with building ordinances which pertain to the locality where the building is to be constructed. Building ordinances should be available for reference when questions arise as to what type of construction is permitted, what are the minimum sizes of materials allowable and similar problems. Sometimes the blueprint will not give exact information on certain parts of the building, the specifications usually stating that all building must conform to the local building ordinances.

To acquire estimating ability is not difficult. Naturally the carpenter must be able to read blueprints; with this as a start the problem resolves itself into one of learning how each part of the building is figured and how the various building materials are purchased.

It must not be overlooked that materials omitted or forgotten are just that much off the profit side of the ledger; a continuance of this loss naturally means failure. If a well thought out systematic plan is used, a complete list of materials can be made and the estimator is assured that nothing has been missed. The plan is to graphically divide a residence project into definite classifications, these divisions again being divided into units. It then only becomes necessary to think carefully through one unit at a time, study the specifications for the kind and grade of material and list the pieces or quantities required.

ESTIMATING DIVISIONS FOR RESIDENCE WORK

The five major divisions into which a dwelling can be divided with the units for each are as follows:

Division	Units
Foundation	*Concrete forms, concrete materials, common brick and concrete blocks*
Framing	*Underpinning, floors, walls, ceiling, roof, stairs*
Exterior Finish	*Frames, walls, cornice, roofing*
Interior Finish	*Windows, doors, screens and shutters, inside trim, cabinets, floors*
Hardware	*Rough and finish*

Each of these divisions with its respective units will be discussed in detail and in the order given. Naturally there may be methods of construction used by carpenters which will be slightly different than those described. Fundamentally these differences will not affect the quantities of materials needed.

PRELIMINARY STEPS WHEN ESTIMATING

1. The first thing to do when starting to take off a bill of materials is to study the blueprints carefully to get a good mental picture of the building to be constructed. This cannot be done quickly but will take time as it is important to know what the construction is to be, how the exterior is to be finished, the kind of roofing required, the shape of the roof, what the interior details are and numerous other facts which all serve as a background.

2. The specifications that pertain to the carpenter's work should next be read carefully and specification page numbers listed for quick reference. At this reading it is not necessary to remember all details of construction or sizes of materials but it is done merely to get a general knowledge of the contents and how to find the information quickly.

3. The third important step before actually beginning to list the materials is to check the main dimensions and figure the perimeter of the building. Perimeter is the term used for the distance around a rectangle or square. It is also well to make a count of the number of doors and windows. The total floor area should also be figured, dividing it into three parts—the total floor area, the area of the bathroom, which usually is tiled, and the areas of the kitchen and porch, which usually do not have hardwood floors.

MEASUREMENT CHECK-UP SHEET

The following measurement check-up sheet is practical and useful when estimating. Time will be saved if each item shown is figured and amounts listed as these measurements are used often when taking off a bill of materials. Fully as important, the estimator will find he is quite well informed about the plan to be figured; all of the different parts of the plans and elevations will be well fixed in his mind by the time the sheet is filled out. See page 5.

MATERIALS TO BE ESTIMATED

Materials needed in the construction of a house, as far as a carpenter is concerned, are concrete materials, lumber, building paper, millwork, and hardware.

ESTIMATING PRACTICES FOR LUMBER

All lumber is *purchased* on the basis of either the board foot or square foot. The terms "board foot" and "square foot" are loosely used in the lumber industry, one often being substituted for the other. Actually, however, "board foot" should be used only when computing the price of rough lumber. "Square foot" should be applied to stock that is to be milled, such as siding, T&G flooring and T&G ceiling.

The term "board foot" means a piece of lumber one inch thick, 12 inches wide and 12 inches long. A piece of lumber having other dimensions is changed, mathematically, into board feet by dividing the width by 12 and multiplying by the length.

If the lumber is thicker than one inch the same procedure is followed by using the thickness as given.

CHECK-UP MEASUREMENT SHEET

Job .... Estimator............... .... Date. ....

DIMENSIONS

Dim. of House ....   First Story Ceil. Height ....
Dim. of Garage ....   Second Story Ceil. Height ....
    (Attached or Detached)   Linear Ft. Cornice ....
Perimeter ....   No. of Piers ....

FLOOR AREAS

Total House Area ....
   (No Porch)
Less Garage (Attached) ....
House Area Only ....
Covered Porch ....
Open Porch ....
   Total ....
Garage if detached ....

Unit Areas

Cement Floors:
   Garage ....
   Porches ....
   Basement ....
   Total ....
Linoleum ....
Hardwood ....
Tile ....

FRAMES — VENTS
CASED OPENINGS

Gable or Attic Vents ....
Foundation Vents ....
Window Frames ....
Door Frames ....
Inside Door Openings ....
Cased Openings ....
Garage Doors:
   Overhead ....
   Hinged ....
Frames (Check correct one):
   Steel ....
   Wood ....
   Open-in ....
   Open-out ....
   Double-Hung ....

WALL MEASUREMENTS

Ext. Walls	Int. Walls
First Fl.	First Fl. ....
Second Fl.	Second Fl. ......
Garage	Garage ....
Total	*Total* ....

Total Lin. Ft. all Walls ....

Wall Areas

Exterior Walls ....
Interior Walls ....
   Total Area All Walls ....

ROOF AREAS

Plan Area:
   House ....
   Garage ....
   Porch ....
Cornice Plan Area ....
   Total Plan Area ....
Roof Pitch ....
Pitch Increase (See page 60) ......
   Total Roof Area ....

SASH — DOORS — C. C. DOORS
— DRAWERS

....Window & Sash (Pieces) ......
....Outside Doors (Pieces) ....
....Inside Doors (Pieces) ....
....Inside Screens ....
....Shutters ....
....C. C. Doors ....
....Drawers & Bins ....
....Cooler Shelves ....
....Mantel Shelf ....

Lumber less than one inch thick is counted as a full inch.

How many board feet of lumber are there is 3 pieces of 1″ x 8″ — 18′ and 16 pieces 2″ x 4″ — 22′?

$$\frac{3 \times 1 \times 8 \times 18}{12} = 36 \text{ board feet}$$

$$\frac{16 \times 2 \times 4 \times 22}{12} = 234\tfrac{2}{3} \text{ board feet}$$

When *estimating* lumber the term "square foot" is often used. A square foot of lumber is 12″ x 12″ (or equivalent area) irrespective of its thickness. Siding, for example, is estimated by the square foot, as it varies in thickness from ½″ to ¾″. Three-ply paneling is estimated on the square foot basis as it varies in thickness from ¼″ to ¾″. Ordering by the square foot requires additional material to be added to the square foot of surface, to allow for the waste incurred in milling.

HOW TO DETERMINE THE ORDERING UNIT FOR LUMBER

There are certain practices followed by a carpenter when determining the ordering unit for lumber, as follows:

1. All lumber is bought on the basis of the number of pieces, linear feet, board feet, square feet or bundles.

   A. Order lumber by the piece if:

      (a) each end rests on bearings that are a stated distance apart, or

      (b) a number of pieces are required that are the same length, or

(c) a definite length is needed to cut without waste.

B. Order by the linear foot of the stock is to be cut into several lengths, or if it can be joined almost anywhere. (Bottom plates, for example.)

C. Order by the board foot if an area is to be covered with rough lumber which can be joined almost anywhere. Sub-floor on joists, for example.

D. Order by the square foot when the lumber has been milled, such as flooring, ceiling, siding, and 3-ply paneling.

E. Order by the bundle when the material can only be purchased in that way. Lath is an example.

2. The kind and grade, or quality, of lumber is indicated in the specifications which should always be checked before writing out an order.

3. All increases in the number of board feet or square feet of stock required to cover a given area, are based on the method of laying it and the waste incurred in milling. These increases will vary for each kinds of material.

4. All fractional parts of a linear or board foot of lumber are counted as another foot.

5. All odd number of lengths of lumber are increased to the next even foot unless two pieces are coming into an even foot length of stock.

NOTE: Because of their interest in conserving the lumber supply, lumber dealers are cooperating with the United States Government in its desire

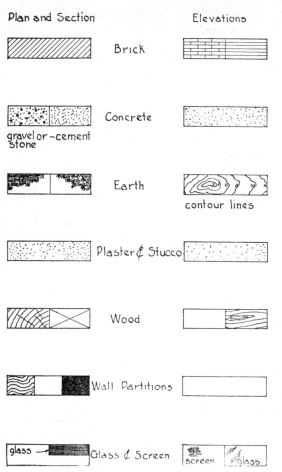

FIG. 1—*Symbols of Materials*

to utilize short lengths of lumber. It is more economical to buy lumber in short lengths, and therefore an advantage for an estimator to watch for opportunities to order lumber on this basis. Short lengths of lumber will not accumulate rapidly on a job if the estimating has been done efficiently, so that it is safe practice to include some "shorts" on a house lumber bill.

FRACTIONAL MEASUREMENTS ON THE BLUEPRINT

To simplify the work of figuring perimeters, areas, and similar mathematical situations the estimator rarely handles a fractional number. The rule is to increase all fractional measurements to the next half or whole foot before computing.

PLAN SYMBOLS

There are a number of recognized standard symbols used in architectural drawings to represent the different building materials. Figure 1 indicates some of those more commonly used for the different kinds of materials.

PLAN INDICATIONS

Figures 2 and 3 illustrate plan indications for doors and windows. These are not always shown or drawn in exactly the same way, but the basic representation is usually evident.

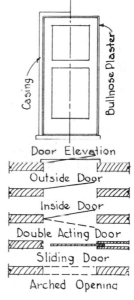

Fig. 2—*Door Symbols*

SPECIFICATIONS

The term specification, as applied to a building job, refers to a written description of materials required to construct a building.

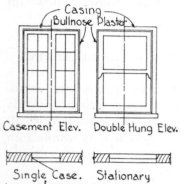

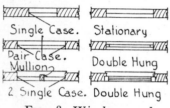

Fig. 3—*Window and Sash Symbols*

Labor requirements are also described. Standards of quality which must be followed in both materials and workmanship are indicated. There is a very definite tie-up or relationship between a set of specifications and a blueprint. In architectural work, the plans and specifications are intended to cooperate and anything shown or mentioned in one must be furnished, even though not mentioned in the other.

An analysis of a set of specifications reveals the following general information:

The kind of materials to be used.

The grade of these materials.

The sizes of the materials.

The kind of workmanship acceptable.

The responsibilities of the contractor, subcontractors, and owner in practically all matters.

The time limits of the contract.

It should be evident that one cannot intelligently read a blueprint and take-off a bill of materials without continued reference to the specifications.

ABBREVIATIONS

A knowledge of abbreviations is important and essential in reading the plans. Some of those in common usage are:

av., average
bd., board
bd. ft., board feet; a piece one foot square by one inch thick
bev., beveled
bldg., building
b. m., board measure
c. c., center to center
clg., ceiling
clr., clear
c., center line
com., common
cas., casing
cu. ft., cubic foot
dim., dimension
D. A., double acting
D. H., double hung
d. s., drop siding
D.F., Douglas Fir
e., edge
flg., flooring
f. o. k., free of knots
hdwd., hardwood
hrt., heart
in., inch or inches
k. d., kiln dried or "knocked down"
lbr., lumber
lgth., length
lin. ft., linear foot (12 inches)
L. P., Loose pin
lth., lath

lt., light
M., thousand
MBF., thousand board feet
mldg., moulding
M. R., mill run
MSM., thousand feet surface measure
No., number
N. P., Nickel plate
Ord., order
O. B. S. D., open bottom screen door
o. c., on center
p., pattern
P. B. S. D., panel bottom screen door
qtd., quartered (hardwoods)
Rwd., redwood
r. c., round corner
rdm., random
res., resawed
reg., register
rfg., roofing
rad., radiator
R. Sdg., rustic siding
S1E. (sized) surfaced one edge
S2S., surfaced two edges
S1S., surfaced one side
S1S1E., surfaced one side and one edge
S2S1E., surfaced two sides and one edge

S4S., surfaced four sidees
sap., sapwood
sd., seasoned
sdg., siding
sel., select
sm., surface measure
snd., sound
S. P., sugar pine
sq., square
std., standard
stk., stock
stp., stepping
T&G., tongued and grooved

TB&S., top, bottom, and sides
V1S., V one side (a longitudinal V-shaped groove on one face of a piece of lumber)
V2S., V two sides
VCV., V and center V
V. G., vertical grain
wth., width
wt., weight
W. P., white pine
x, by, as 2 x 4

CHECK-UP PROCEDURE

An experienced estimator will use a colored pencil or crayon and check-off each item on the blue print as soon as it has been figured or estimated. This procedure also permits a quick re-check at any time to see that no items have been overlooked.

NOTE: The carpenter apprentice should carefully study Chapter X as a preliminary to actually "taking-off" a bill of materials as the various mensuration rules used by an estimator are explained in detail in this chapter.

CHAPTER II

FOUNDATION MATERIALS

THE ESTIMATOR'S work on residential foundations is applied to four situations, concrete forms, concrete materials, common brick and concrete blocks.

CONCRETE FORM UNIT

A concrete wall form is necessary whenever a concrete wall is to be built. See Figure 4. It is composed

FIG. 4—*Typical Concrete Foundation Forms for a House Without Basement*

of horizontal boards, braces, whalers, stakes and tie wire. See Figure 5.

Boards 1″ x 6″ surfaced on one side, S1S, are usually selected for form boards. Sometimes the sub-floor ma-

terial is used and then cleaned thoroughly before nailing down for the rough floor. If the concrete wall is
not to be plastered then the boards are laid with the
smooth side in so that the concrete will have a smooth

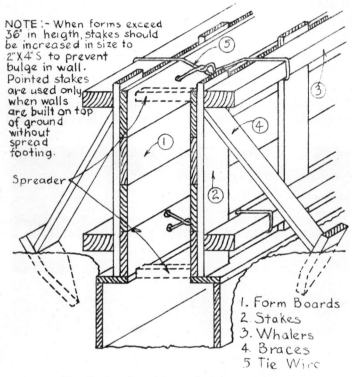

NOTE :- When forms exceed
36" in height, stakes should
be increased in size to
2"X4"S to prevent
bulge in wall.
Pointed stakes
are used only
when walls
are built on top
of ground
without
spread
footing.

Spreader

1. Form Boards
2. Stakes
3. Whalers
4. Braces
5 Tie Wire

FIG. 5—*Section Through Concrete Form*

appearance. Occasionally matched flooring is used if a
particularly good job is wanted. When the concrete
wall is to be plastered then forms are placed with the
rough side of the boards in; the concrete wall will then

present a rough texture on which plaster material will adhere more readily.

These 1" x 6" boards are laid horizontally and held in place by stakes of varying sizes. 1" material is often used. For a basement wall form studs are used instead of stakes. These are placed vertically; often a complete panel will be built and then placed in position.

To strengthen the form, braces and whalers are used. A whaler is a piece of lumber, usually 2" x 4", placed horizontally against the outside face of the stakes to hold the form true and straight. For an ordinary foundation one whaler only is needed for each side of the concrete form. Tie wires are used to hold the form from spreading while the concrete is being placed.

While not a part of the form itself the bolts that are used to hold down the sill are usually figured at the time that the form material is listed.

Each of the parts of a form may be figured as follows:

FORM BOARDS

The height of a form is figured on the basis of 6" boards. 10" height would require two boards; 16", three boards; 24", four boards, etc.

> *Rule*: To find the board feet of lumber for one wall of a form, multiply the height of the form, in terms of 6" boards, by the length, which for a residence would be the perimeter* of the building. Then add ⅕ for waste. Doubling this amount will give the necessary material for both forms.

NOTE: In figuring perimeters, fractional parts of a building are increased to the next half or whole foot.
*See page 234.

To illustrate, 54'-8" would be called 55'-0". Any fractional answer is also increased to a whole number. In the case of lumber, it is increased to a whole *even* number as lumber is always cut to even foot lengths.

STAKES

No definite rule can be laid down for stakes. Common practice in some areas places them two feet on center (o.c.). The length is the same as the height of the form plus a sufficient amount for a point.

Rule: To find the number divide perimeter by the spacing of the stakes. Then add one; then double.

FORM STUDS

Form studs are spaced at different distances apart depending on the height of the form. They are located in a vertical position and 1" x 6" form boards are nailed to them. The size of the lumber is determined by the height of the form.

Rule: To find the number of studs, divide the perimeter by the spacing of the studs and add one extra; then double this result for the other form. This will give the number of uprights required. The length of each will be as long as the form is high. Mutiply the number of studs by the length of each; then order that many linear feet of stock; order lengths which will cut with the least waste.

WHALERS

A whaler is a piece of framing stock 2" x 4" or 2" x 6" placed horizontally on the outside of a form against the form studs to hold them to a true and straight line and give rigidity.

Rule: Find the perimeter of the building and then double it, as each form will require a whaler. This will give enough material for one whaler. Multiply the result by the number of whalers.*

BRACES

No brace material is ordered for an average foundation as contractors save odds and ends of lumber for this purpose. 1" x 6" form boards are sometimes cut to short lengths and split to 1" x 3".

TIE WIRE

Tie wire is used on wood forms to hold them from spreading when the concrete is being poured. See figure 5. It is bought by the pound and comes in flat rolls. For an average job a roll is usually bought.

Tie wires are placed at varying distances apart, depending on the height of the forms and the thickness of the wall. They are placed on an average, about 4' apart, horizontally and 2' apart vertically. The length of each piece of wire will be twice the thickness of the wall plus sufficient wire to go around each stake and whaler. For an 8" wall each piece should be at least 60" long.

To change linear feet of wire to pounds use the following table:

TABLE I
WIRE SIZES AND WEIGHTS

Size of Wire	Weight per Linear Foot	Feet per Pound
No. 11	.0387	25.82
No. 12	.0296	33.69
No. 13	.0223	44.98

*Whalers are *vertically* spaced approximately 2' for a high wall.

> *Rule*: Multiply number of pieces of wire required
> by the length of each. Then multiply by the weight
> per foot of the size wire specified. Result equals
> pounds of wire necessary for the job.

BOLTS

Specifications and building ordinances vary regarding the size and spacing of bolts used to hold the sill down to the foundation. 6′ on centers is common practice and the size often required is ½″ x 8″ carriage bolts.

> *Rule*: To find the number divide the perimeter of
> the building by the bolt spacing; add one extra
> bolt for each corner or angle. The result equals
> the number of bolts. As these are priced by the
> dozen it is good business to order on that basis.

NAILS

A 6d box nail is best and for an average foundation twelve to fifteen pounds of these box nails would be required. There should also be a few pounds of 8d box nails ordered.

The point to remember in nailing is that the form must be made straight, plumb and very rigid. The nails must not be too long as a form can be so well nailed that either the form material is spoiled when taking the form down or the concrete wall itself may be cracked or chipped. Often the nails are not driven in tight so they can be easily pulled.

NOTE: It is good practice to let one board extend several inches beyond the corner at right angles to it. Then a vertical cleat is nailed on this extension. This makes a corner that will hold well and yet is easily removed. See figure 6.

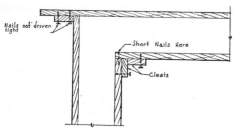

FIG. 6—*Typical Corner of a Form Construction*

SPREADERS

Spreaders are needed to keep concrete forms properly spaced. Sometimes both forms are strongly braced and 1″ x 1″ pieces of wood cut to a length equal to wall thickness are placed at various locations in the form. These are removed as the concrete is poured. A better spreader is made of metal and acts both as a tie and spreader. When these are used the outside form is strongly braced and the inside form braced only a little as the metal tie and speader holds it rigidly to the outside form. Local dealers should be consulted as there are several types available and the number required for a job is based on the type selected.

LINSEED OIL

Specifications sometimes call for concrete forms to be oiled before the concrete is placed. This is usually done when the finished concrete wall is not to be plastered.

Rule: One gallon of oil will cover approximately 600 square feet of surface. Total linear feet of wall times height equals square feet of area in one form. Double this for both forms. Divide result by 600. Answer equals gallons of oil required.

CONCRETE MATERIAL UNIT

The term concrete is used to denote a properly proportioned mixture of cement, sand and rock. The

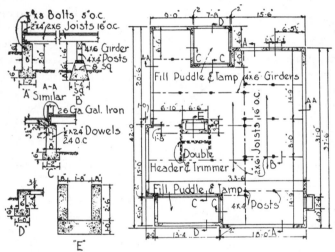

Fig. 7—*A Concrete Foundation Plan*

proportions will vary according to the load to be carried. In general the assumed compressive strength of concrete is about 2,000 pounds per square inch at 28 days and greater strength is secured by increasing the size of the foundation wall thickness rather than changing proportions of the mix.

FOUNDATION PARTS

The parts of a foundation are footings, walls, dwarf walls, and piers. A footing is that part which is put in the ground first to act as a base for the foundation. It is wide but not very thick, as its purpose is to provide a good bearing for the building. The wall is built on top of the footing. A dwarf wall is any continuous wall inside the foundations. Piers are blocks of concrete used to support posts. Figure 7 illustrates a typical foundation plan.

CONSTRUCTION METHODS

The construction of a foundation will vary in different parts of the country. In the West a basement is seldom constructed. The full basement, covering the area of the house, is common in the northern and eastern parts of the United States. Basement walls must therefore be included as part of a complete foundation.

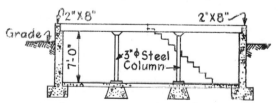

Fig. 8—*Illustrating Round Columns*

If a residence has a full basement it may have supporting concrete columns. These columns are constructed by filling a round heavy metal casing with concrete. See figure 8.

The depth of a foundation wall below the grade will vary, a foot or two being quite sufficient in warm climates, providing the soil has good bearing qualities, while in a cold climate it is necessary to extend the concrete footing below the frost line.

UNIT OF MEASURE

The unit of measure, when estimating quantities of concrete, is either the cubic yard or cubic foot, the former being used on large concrete jobs. The cubic foot measurement is best for residence work. When ordering the sand and rock change the cubic feet of material to cubic yards or tons depending upon the local practice.

ALLOWANCE FOR VOIDS

More sand and rock are required than the actual content of the form. This is due to the voids between the rocks which must be filled. The spaces between the particles of sand, minute as they are, must also be filled. The process of mixing these ingredients together, with the proper amount of water, using the cement as a binder, causes these voids to be filled, the resulting concrete becoming a solid, compact mass which will take less space than before mixing.

No exact rule can be given that will indicate how much more material must be ordered to allow for the shrinkage. The proportion of sand and rock and the size of the rock are factors that affect the fractional part to be added. However, a rule can be given that will give accurate results for an average size dwelling foundation. There are several definite steps to be followed.

1. FIGURING THE CONTENT OF THE FORM*

Rule for footing and walls: Mutiply the width of
the form expressed in feet (as 8/12 for a form 8″
*See tables on pages 160, 161.

wide) by the depth, expressed in feet as (16/12 for a form 16″ deep) by the length of the form, usually the perimeter of the building. Footings and walls must each be figured separately.

Rule for basement walls: Basement walls are estimated the same as a foundation wall. Figure the perimeter of the basement; multiply by the height of the wall and then by the wall thickness. The *outside* dimensions of the basement are used to find the perimeter. Mathematically this will give a little more than the actual form content due to doubling up at the corners; this extra material is offset by the loss incurred in handling the concrete materials as a certain amount of waste is unavoidable.

Rule for round columns: To figure a round column (sometimes known as a "lally" column) multiply the cross section area (diameter squared times .7854 equals area) by the height of the column.

Rule for piers: Concrete piers are of various shapes and sizes. Some times they are larger at the bottom than the top. To find cubic footage for a tapered pier add the top and bottom areas together, divide by 2; then multiply by the height. This is not an exact mathematical procedure but is sufficiently close for all practical purposes. If a large number of piers are involved 5% should be added.

If the pier is square multiply area or the base by pier height to find cubic feet.

If the pier is round multiply the cross section area (diameter squared by .7854 equals area) by the pier height.

All dimensions used should be in feet. If dimensions are figured in inches the total result must be divided by 1728 to change to cubic feet.

2. ALLOWING FOR SHRINKAGE DUE TO VOIDS

After the actual content of the footings, walls and piers is figured, allowance must be made for extra material. If a concrete table is used the shrinkage is automatically allowed.

TABLE II
CONCRETE TABLE

Mix	Cement (in sacks)	Sand (cubic feet)	Rock (¾″ and under) (cubic feet)
1:2:3	.23	.47	.73
1:2:4	.20	.41	.81
1:2:4½	.18	.38	.86
1:3:4	.17	.52	.72
1:2½:5	.16	.42	.83

Rule: Selecting the correct mix, read the constants that represent cement, sand and rock, and multiply the actual content of the forms by each of these numbers. Convert rock and sand to cubic yards or tons.

3. CONVERTING SAND AND ROCK TO TONS OR CUBIC YARDS

The rule is based on the assumption that a cubic foot of either weighs 100 pounds. The weight of sand or rock will vary, particularly the former, as some sand contains more water, which increase its weight.

Rule 1: To change cubic feet to cubic yards, divide by 27, the number of cubic feet in one cubic yard.

Rule 2: To change cubic feet to tons divide by 20. A fractional yard or ton is generally increased to a half or whole yard or ton.

4. CEMENT CONTRACTORS' METHODS

A practical method used by cement contractors will give quite accurate results. This rule automatically allows for shrinkage.

Proceed as follows:

Rule: a. Find cubic feet contents of footings, walls and piers.

    b. Divide the cubic footage by 15. Result equals tonnage of concrete aggregate (sand and rock combined). Material dealers will furnish concrete aggregate in several proportions, such as 50-50 or 40-60, etc.

    c. To find sacks of cement multiply tonnage of aggregate by a constant selected from table III.

TABLE III

AGGREGATE TABLE

Mix	Aggregate Mix	Constant
1-2-3	1-5	4
1-2-4	1-6	$3\frac{1}{2}$
1-3-4	1-7	3
1-3-5	1-8	$2\frac{1}{2}$

COMMON BRICK UNIT

BRICK FOUNDATIONS

On many residences brick are used for foundation walls, a concrete footing being placed first and then brick walls constructed on this footing.

Brick are estimated on the basis of their size. The measuring units are one square foot of wall surface and the number of brick per square foot of surface. A brick contractor should be consulted to find extra amounts of masonry materials necessary to construct a foundation wall.

The following table indicates the number of standard size bricks per square foot of wall based on the thickness of the wall and of the mortar joints.

TABLE IV

NUMBER OF COMMON BRICK PER SQUARE FOOT OF WALL SURFACE*

Thickness of Wall in Inches	Number of Bricks Thick	Thickness of Mortar Joints in Inches					
		$\frac{1}{8}$ in.	$\frac{1}{4}$ in.	$\frac{1}{2}$ in.	$\frac{3}{8}$ in.	$\frac{3}{4}$ in.	$\frac{5}{8}$ in.
4 or 4½	1	7½	7	6½	6$\frac{1}{16}$	5⅞	5½
8 or 9	2	15	14	13	12⅓	11¾	11
12 or 13	3	22½	21	19½	18½	17⅝	16½
16 or 17	4	30	28	26	24⅔	23½	22
20 or 21	5	37½	35	32½	30⅚	29⅜	27½
24 or 25	6	45	42	39	37	35¼	33

*For a brick sidewalk allow 4½ bricks for each *square* foot of walk.

Rule: To find number of brick required multiply the total linear feet of foundation wall by the wall height. Then multiply the result by the number of brick per square foot as selected from the table, on the basis of thickness of the wall and of the mortar joints. Answer equals number of brick. It is advisable to increase the number 2 or 3% to allow for breakage in handling.

Brick are priced on the thousand basis. Therefore change the number of brick required into the "thousand" unit, or a fraction of it, such as one quarter or one half.

MORTAR

A general rule only can be given for mortar as the amount required varies with the thickness of the joints and the size of the brick.

TABLE V
QUANTITY OF MORTAR REQUIRED FOR 1000 STANDARD SIZE COMMON BRICK

Size of the Joint	$\frac{1}{8}''$	$\frac{1}{4}''$	$\frac{3}{8}''$	$\frac{1}{2}''$	$\frac{5}{8}''$
Cubic Feet of Mortar	7	$9\frac{1}{2}$	$12\frac{1}{2}$	15	18

Rule: Divide the number of brick required by 1000 and multiply by a constant selected from above table, and based on the thickness of mortar joint specified. Then divide by 27. Results equals number of cubic yards of mortar. Part of a yard is usually increased to a whole number.

CONCRETE BLOCK UNIT

CONCRETE BLOCKS

Concreate blocks are used in the same manner as brick in order to make an ornamental foundation. They vary in width from 8″ to 12″ their thickness being 8″ and length 16″.

The following table indicates the number of blocks required for 100 square feet of wall surface.

TABLE VI

NUMBER OF CONCRETE BLOCKS PER SQUARE
(100 square feet)

Size of Blocks	Thickness of Wall	No. Blocks per Square
8″ x 8″ x 16″	8″	110
8″ x 10″ x 16″	10″	110
8″ x 8″ x 16″	12″	110

Rule: Multiply wall length by its height to get square feet of wall surface. Then deduct area of all openings. Divide by 100 to change to "squares." Multiply number of squares by 110. Result equals number of concrete blocks required.

NOTE: Exact wall measurements should be used and the corners not counted twice.

MORTAR

Rule: Allow $3\frac{1}{4}$ cubic feet of mortar for every 100 square feet of wall area. Divide total number of cubic feet by 27 to change to cubic yards. Order full yards of mortar.

CHAPTER III

FRAMING

FRAMING MATERIALS for house construction include all structural members framed together to form the framework of a building. The lumber used is rough material, which has been ripped or sized to make it standard, and is commonly called "dimension" lumber.

The framework of a residence can be divided into five groups. Following the usual constructional order, first comes the underpinning which includes all materials below the first floor. The second division is the floor; the third the walls and partitions; the fourth pertains to the ceilings, and lastly, comes the roof. On a two-story house there is a sixth division, namely, the stairs.

The carpenter when estimating, is rarely concerned with the thickness and width of lumber, as he reads the blueprints and specifications to find these dimensions.

The thickness and width of lumber for the different framing members will vary according to building ordinance requirements and the load to be carried. The kind and grade of the lumber is usually stated in the specifications.

UNDERPINNING UNIT

Underpinning is the term used to include all framing materials that support the first floor joists. The several parts are sill, cribbing studs and plates, pier blocks, posts, girders and braces.

SILL

Sill is the lumber laid on top of a concrete or brick foundation wall to provide a nailing surface for the floor joists. In good construction it is bolted down as shown in figure 9.

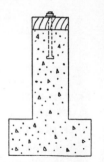

Sometimes a building is constructed with a continuous concrete wall on the inside of the foundation instead of using piers. This is known as a dwarf wall and will also require mudsills. See figure 10.

FIG. 9—*Foundation Sill Bolted Down*

In the western part of the United States, redwood or treated lumber is always used for sill stock as moisture does not rot or warp it. Cypress and cedar also have the same qualifications.

> *Rule*: Figure the perimeter of the building; add all dwarf walls. Result equals linear feet of sill required. Thickness and width of lumber measurements are given in the specifications or on the blueprint.*

PIER BLOCKS

A pier block is cut square and placed directly on a concrete pier. If its size is similar to the sill, the number of feet of material required for these blocks is added to the sill order. Read the blueprint for size.

> *Rule*: Count the number of piers on the foundation plan; determine the length of one block, multiply

*For a small building, such as a garage, order lengths of lumber which are the same as the width and length dimensions of the building.

by the number of piers, then change to an **even** number of feet.

Fig. 10—*Concrete Foundation Showing Dwarf Walls*

CRIBBING PLATES

A cribbing plate is necessary if the first floor joists are not placed directly on the concrete foundation. This type of construction is used when the foundation is "stepped" so as to conform to the grade of the lot. The best construction requires foundation walls to be high enough to receive the joists.

Rule: If a single plate is specified, figure the perimeter of the building. Include all dwarf walls. Results equal linear feet for one plate. If more than one plate is specified, multiply the above result by the number of plates. Thickness and width measurements of the lumber will be given on the plans.

CRIBBING STUDS

The number of studs required to form the framework to support first floor joists varies with their spacing. The length of each will vary according to the slope of the lot or the steps in the foundation.

Rule to find the number of cribbing studs: Multiply the total length of all exterior walls and dwarf walls by the spacing constant of the studs.

Use the following table for spacing problems. Multiply the linear distance by the constant that represents the spacing.

TABLE VII

SPACING TABLE

Spacing	Constant
12″	1
16″	$\frac{3}{4}$
18″	$\frac{2}{3}$
20″	$\frac{3}{5}$
24″	$\frac{1}{2}$

NOTE: Always add one to number obtained this way, for the "starter."

The length of the studs will be read on the blueprint. If the foundation is "stepped" find the average length of each stud by adding the shortest and longest lengths together and dividing by 2. If the shortest stud is 10″ and the longest 38″ the average would be $\dfrac{10'' \text{ plus } 38''}{2}$ or 24″.

Rule to find linear feet: Multiply the number of studs by their average length. Order that many linear feet of lumber or order the material by the piece, selecting a length which will cut with the least waste.

POSTS

Posts are necessary on top of each pier block to form a support for the girders. See figure 11. Count on the foundation plan the number of piers allowing one post for each pier. The length of the posts will vary. The size stock will vary according to the load to be carried and the ordinance requirements.

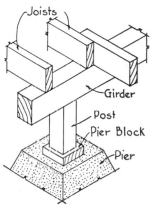

Fig. 11—*Girders and Posts Required for First Floor Joist Supports*

Rule: Find the average length of each post. (See cribbing studs above.) Read the plan carefully for special lengths. Multiply average length of each post by the number of posts and order that many linear feet of lumber or change to lengths which will cut without waste. Special basement posts will be ordered by the piece and should not be combined with the regular pier posts.

Note: It is good trade practice, if posts and girders are of the same size, to order post material the same lengths as the girder stock. The foreman carpenter can then select the straightest stock for the girders and cut up the bowed pieces for posts.

GIRDERS*

Girders are placed horizontally inside the foundation to form a bearing for first floor joists and are supported by posts placed on the piers. The size of the stock varies according to the load to be carried and the spacing of the posts. Building codes give minimum requirements. 4″ x 6″ lumber is often used. Larger sizes are needed if the building has a full basement.

> *Rule*: The length of a girder is determined by using an architect's scale and measuring the distance from pier to pier as shown on the foundation plan. Then order lengths that will join on a pier. An average foundation will require several different lengths.

BRACES

Few braces are necessary in the underpinning of a modern dwelling, particularly if the concrete foundation is high enough for the joists to bear directly on it. When cribbing studs are used, each corner should have two braces placed at a 45 degree angle. On a long wall additional braces should be figured, checking the local building ordinance for all requirements. Sometimes a brace is nailed parallel to a joist, the lower end being nailed to the bottom of a cribbing stud.

> *Rule*: Figure length of the cribbing studs and find the diagonal of a right angle whose altitude and base are the same as this length. The carpenter's

*If the house has a full basement the girders are larger and less posts are used; however, the rule will still apply.

steel square can be used to do this. See figure 12. Allow two pieces to a corner and at least one extra piece for every 25 linear feet of wall. Combine into standard lengths or order by the linear foot.

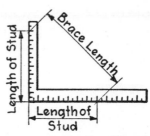

Fig. 12—*Application of Steel Square to Find Brace Length*

For braces parallel to the joists estimate the length of one piece; figure the number of pieces required according to the specifications. Order lengths which will cut with the least waste.

FLOOR UNIT

The several parts of the floor unit are joists, header joists, solid and herringbone bridging, sub-floor, and building paper. These terms are applied to first and second floors, in fact they are used to describe any floor of a framed building.

FLOOR JOISTS

Floor joists are framing members placed in a horizontal direction to receive the sub-floor. See figure 13. They are carried by girders and outside walls for the first floor, and bearing partitions and outside walls for the second floor.

The thickness of joist stock is never less than 2″ and rarely more unless some special construction is designed. The width of the lumber varies according to the span, the wider span requiring wider joists. The number of pieces of lumber required for floor joists will vary with the spacing. In good construction additional joists are required as each parallel cross partition should have a floor joist under it.

FIG. 13—*Setting First Floor Joists*

Rule: The lengths of first floor joists are scaled on the foundation plan. For the second floor joists the first floor plan is scaled. All joists must be long enough to bear on either a girder or bearing partition. Read the specifications for the amount of lap required if joists are not continuous. An average residence requires several different lengths of lumber for the joists. The direction of first floor joists is at right angles to the girders. The blueprint should be carefully studied for the direction of second floor joists. Joists should span the short way of a room if possible.

To find the number of joists, multiply length of the wall that carries the floor joists by the joist spacing constant. (See table VII, page 32 for spacing constants.) This will give the number of spaces, a fractional space being counted as a full one. Then add one. Also add one extra piece for every partition that runs parallel to the joists. This will give the number of joists required. This process is repeated for each outside bearing wall of the building.

HEADER JOISTS

A header joist is a continuous piece of lumber either nailed on the outside end of the joists or cut in between each joist. Headers must also be cut in between joists at each girder, over which a partition is built, and over each bearing partition. Its purpose is to close the space between the ends of the joists and also keep them from twisting.

The size of the header is always the same as that of the joists.

Rule: *1st floor*—The linear feet of all outside* bearing walls plus the linear feet of all girders over which partitions are built equals the linear feet of header stock.

2nd floor—The linear feet of all outside bearing walls plus the linear feet of all bearing partitions equals the linear feet of header stock.

BRIDGING

In order to strengthen and make more rigid a set of floor joists, framing lumber called bridging is cut and nailed between the joists, placing each row at equal distances across the span. Sometimes only one row of

*The wall on which the outside ends of the joists rest is known as a "bearing wall."

bridging is required in which case the span is divided in two parts. When two rows of bridging are specified, the span must be divided into three equal parts. Bridging is usually required for second floor joists and for first floor joists that span a basement.

FIG. 14—*Herringbone Bridging*

There are two kinds of bridging: solid and herringbone. Solid bridging is really another set of headers the same size as the joist stock. Herringhone bridging is made from 2″ x 3″ or 2″ x 4″ and is cut in such a way that each pair of bridging forms a small truss, which prevents the joists from sagging. See figure 14.

Rule for Solid Bridging: The length of the wall on which the joists bear equals the linear feet required for one row of solid bridging. The specifications should be consulted to find the number of rows required. Repeat for all rooms listed in the specifications.

Rule for Herringbone Bridging: Determine the width of the joists. Read specifications for joist spacing. Then multiply the linear feet of distance to be bridged by a constant selected from the following table. Result equals linear feet of lumber to order to make one row. Multiply result by number of rows of bridging required.

TABLE VIII

HERRINGBONE BRIDGING TABLE*

Size of Joists	Spacing	
	12″ o.c.	16″ o.c.
2″ x 6″	2.00	2.00
2″ x 8″	2.30	2.10
2″ x 10″	2.50	2.30
2″ x 12″	2.70	2.40
2″ x 14″	2.90	2.50
2″ x 16″	3.20	2.70

*Using the constants gives enough material for *one row* of bridging consisting of *two pieces* of cross bridging for each joist piece.

NOTE: Bridging can be laid off by using the carpenter's steel square. See figure 15.

The bridging cut problem is simply one of rise and run. As shown on the drawing the rise of the bridging is not the actual width of the joist stock but is at least 2″ less than that width.

The run is equal to the width of the spacing between the joists.

For a floor using a 2″ x 10″ joist, set 16″ o.c., the run would be 14 in. while the rise would be 7½ in.

As the exact difference between distances B and C of the drawing is not know until one piece of the bridging is cut so that the length of the plumb cut can be measured, the simplest way is to assume that the width of the joist is the rise of the bridging. Then, using this rise and the spacing as the run, lay off the

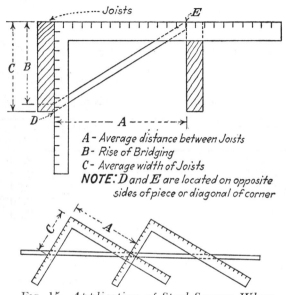

FIG. 15—*Application of Steel Square When Laying Off Herringbone Bridging*

pattern, keeping the rise and run figures on the *opposite* side of the bridging stock. This will automatically take care of the difference between B and C.

Shift the square to its second position and mark another plumb line and the layout of the pattern will be complete.

SUB-FLOOR

Sub-floor material is rough lumber (usually S1S) nailed on top of floor joists to form a solid surface for hardwood flooring. 1″ x 6″ material is often used; occasionally tongue and groove (T&G) stock is specified.

Sub-floor is laid either at right angles to the floor joists or at a 45 degree angle. See figure 16. While the

FIG. 16—*Laying Sub-Floor Diagonally*

diagonal floor is stronger, the main purpose of laying the floor at a 45 degree angle is to permit the hardwood floor to be laid in either direction. This makes it possible to lay a hardwood floor the long way of any room.

The amount of sub-floor needed will vary according to its width and the way it is laid. Specifications must be studied carefully to see which rooms require sub-floor. Often a kitchen or service porch has finished pine floor and no sub-floor.

Several definite steps must be followed when estimating sub-floor. Figure the net area of the surface to be covered. For a rectangular building the width of the building times its length equals area.

When a building is not entirely covered or if there

are angles in the floor layout, the area to be covered can be quickly estimated if a "take-away" method is used.

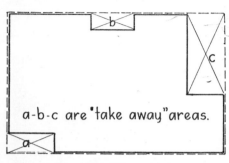

a-b-c are "take away" areas.

FIG. 17—*Illustrating "Take-Away" Areas*

Multiply the largest width dimension of a building by the largest length dimension, as though the building were rectangular. See figure 17. Then find the area of each part that does not require sub-floor material such as a kitchen or porch. Also figure the area of those parts formed by angles and offsets. Add all "take-away" areas and deduct the total amount from the rectangular area. The result is the net area to be covered with sub-floor stock.

To the net area must be added a certain amount of lumber for waste due to sizing the stock or making it T&G and for the end waste caused when laying it. The

TABLE IX
CONSTANT TABLE FOR SUB-FLOOR STOCK

Size of the Stock	1 x 6 not Sized		1 x 6 SISIE to 5½"		1 x 6 T & G Stock 5⅛"	
Method of Laying	Straight	Diagonal	Straight	Diagonal	Straight	Diagonal
Constant	1.1	1.16	1.2	1.3	1.25	1.33

*The *quality* of lumber purchased for sub-floor may necessitate adding to the above constants to assure sufficient stock to do the job. The amount to add must be based on trade judgment as to the lumber quality.

following table gives the fractional amounts to add, and allows for end waste which accumulates when laying sub-floor.

Rule: Multiply floor area by constant given for material used and according to the method of laying. Result equals board feet of lumber required.

BUILDING PAPER

A water-proof sheathing paper is often used on top of a pine floor to keep it clean while plastering the interior of a house. There are several grades and kinds. The standard width of the paper is 36″ and a roll contains 500 square feet. Special kinds of paper or felt can be secured which will vary in width, number of square feet, and weight per roll. Local building material firms can supply this information.

Rule: To find the number of rolls of paper divide the floor area by 500. Broken rolls cannot be purchased, therefore, count part of a roll as a full one.

WALL UNIT

GENERAL FRAMING INFORMATION

There are two types of construction followed in the building of two-story houses; namely, balloon and Western framing. See figure 18. In balloon framing the studs on outside walls are full height from sill to top plate of the second story. In Western framing the first story is framed. Next the second story floor joists are placed and sub-floor laid, after which the second story is framed.

Because of the complexity of layout and construction, an estimator must find some way to simplify the "take-off" work for the walls of a building. Too much

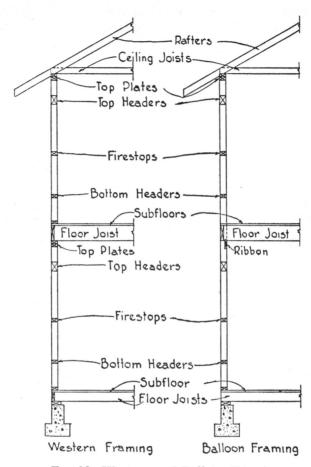

FIG. 18—*Western and Balloon Framing*

time would be consumed if each separate framing member of a wall or partition had to be listed. These framing members are top and bottom plates, studs, braces, and firestops. If only a single opening is considered, top and bottom cripples, top and bottom headers and trimmers must be estimated. See figure 19.

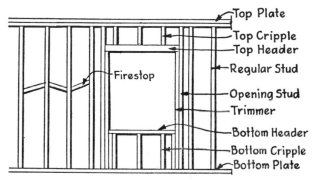

Top Plate
Top Cripple
Top Header
Regular Stud
Opening Stud
Trimmer
Bottom Header
Bottom Cripple
Bottom Plate

Firestop

FIG. 19—*Members of a Framed Wall*

The number of pieces of lumber necessary for some framing members will vary with every wall. A long wall may have no partition backing while a short wall may require two or three pieces. A small opening will have the top header made of the same size stock as the studs, while a wide opening will require a special piece of lumber for the top header. Bracing will also vary in terms of the number of pieces required. Because of these variations, backing, top-headers, and brace materials are each figured separately when listing framing lumber for walls and partitions. The opening framing materials are allowed for by using a general rule which will provide enough material to make them without listing each piece.

The size of framing lumber varies although 2″ x 4″ stock is most commonly used. To secure certain architectural effects a double wall is sometimes built. At least one wall of a bathroom will have 2″ x 6″ studs to provide a wall thick enough to contain the 4″ stack which serves as the main vent for the plumbing system.

Each of the several framing members of a framed wall will be discussed separately and on a basis of either balloon or Western framing.

WESTERN FRAMING
TOP AND BOTTOM PLATES

A plate is the horizontal framing member of a wall or partition at the top and bottom ends of the studs and to which each stud is nailed. The bottom plate is also called a shoe. Two plates are required at the top of the wall, the second one being nailed to place before walls and partitions are plumbed and braced.

Plate stock must be sized to make it the same width throughout and is also surfaced on one side to make it an even thickness. The lumber term for this milling is "S1S1E" (surface one side and one edge).

Rule: Multiply the linear feet of all walls and partitions by the number of plates required (usually three). The result equals the number of linear feet of plate stock required. On residential work the length of walls and partitions varies, consequently random lengths of lumber can be ordered without causing much waste. For a small building such as a garage the rule is: Order lengths of lumber which are the same as the width and length dimensions of the building. Each wall will require two plates if a single top plate is used, or three if the top plate is doubled.

NOTE: When measuring walls and partitions on the blueprint it is a good plan to take the outside walls first and figure the perimeter of the building. Next measure all partitions that run in the same direction, that is: either across the building or else its length; then go across the floor plan in the other direction. This will insure against any partition being overlooked.

STUDS

Studs are vertical members that form the frame work of a wall or partition. See figure 19. They are spaced 16″ on centers (o.c.) to permit the lath to be put on without waste. Wood lath are 48″ long and span four studs. A piece of plaster-board lath is 32″ long and spans three studs.

The length of a stud varies with the height of the ceiling. In many parts of the country, 8′-6″ ceiling height is standard, requiring an 8′ stud. On some two-story houses the first floor will have a 9′ ceiling. This requires a 8′-6″ stud which is cut from either a 9′ piece, if available, or an 18′ piece of lumber.

There are several framing situations to consider when figuring studs such as walls without openings; walls with openings and circular work.

> *Rule for walls without openings*: Multiply the length of the wall or partition by ¾; then add one piece. Result equals number of pieces.

> *Rule for walls with openings*: Allow one stud for each linear foot of wall or partition; then add 20%. This will give enough material to allow for

*Use this rule for figuring garages. Then add extra pieces for opening studs, top headers and braces.

top and bottom cripple studs, bottom headers, trimmers and opening studs.

Rule for circular walls: On circular work studs are usually placed 12″ on center. Allow one stud per foot of wall; then add three studs for every opening. To find length of a wall multiply diameter of the circle by 3.1416.

FIRESTOPS

A firestop may be a piece of framing stock, the same size as the stud material, placed horizontally (or at a slight angle) about half way between the bottom and top plate. See figure 19. In some localities firestops are required to be of brick, concrete or other "fireproof" material; consult your local building code. The purpose is to prevent the creation of a draft in case of a fire between two studs. It also serves as a splendid wall stiffener.

Rule for walls and partitions: Deduct from the total linear feet of walls and partitions the combined width of all openings. Result equals the linear feet of firestops required.

Firestops are also required on all rooms that have cove ceilings to close up the space behind the cove brackets. See figure 20.

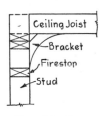

Rule for cove ceilings: Figure the perimeter of each room that has a cove ceiling and order that many linear feet of stock.

FIG. 20—*Cove Bracket*

TOP HEADERS

Top headers are pieces of framing lumber placed horizontally over each opening. They vary in size according to the width of the opening and the load to be carried. Building ordinances usually give minimum requirements.

> *Rule*: Make a list of all openings in the building; add one foot to each width dimension; then combine into lengths which will cut with the least waste. Care should be used when combining lengths to indicate how each is to be cut. This will enable the carpenter foreman to select the correct piece for any opening.

BRACES

A brace is a framing member, cut to as near a 45 degree angle as possible, to stiffen walls and partitions

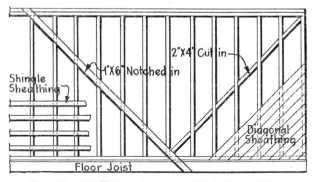

Fig. 21—*Wall Bracing and Wall Sheathing*

of a building and prevent them from collapsing. There are several different ways to cut in a brace. A common method is to use lumber the same size as the studs and cut in a continuous row of braces between several studs. Occasionally a brace is nailed in place first and the studs cut to fit it. Another method now becoming popular and required in some building ordinances is to use a 1" x 4" or 1" x 6" piece of lumber and notch it into the outside face of the studs, making it continuous from the top plate to the sill line. See figure 21.

> *Rule*: Regardless of the method used to frame in the brace, the take-off rule is the same. Find the diagonal of a right angle whose size is equal to the length of the studding. Then increase to a standard length of lumber. All braces are figured at the 45 degree angle even though the angle may have to be less on account of openings in the walls.
>
> The number of braces will vary with the shape and size of a building. Allow two for each corner and one for each main partition. Walls longer than 25' should have one extra brace allowed. It may not be possible to always place two braces at every corner or in every main partition due to the openings; however the extra brace stock can usually be used in some short partition.

WALL BACKING

Backing is framing material required at the intersection of two partitions or every partition and wall so as to permit each room to be lathed separately. See figure 22. Improved construction demands additional studs be used for backing. These studs are nailed in place

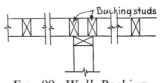

Fig. 22—*Wall Backing*

when the walls and partitions are framed. The lumber is the same size and length as the studding.

Rule: Allow four pieces of stud material for each room and each closet.

BALLOON FRAMING

The preceding rules have been based on Western framing methods in which one story at a time is framed. Additional rules are necessary in balloon framing for outside wall studding and the ribbon used to support second floor joists. For all inside partitions in balloon framing the Western framing rules will also apply.

STUDS FOR BALLOON FRAMING

In balloon framing the studding extends from sill to the top plate of the second story.

Rule: Allow one full length stud for every linear foot of outside wall. The perimeter of the building will usually give the linear feet of wall to be framed. The length of these studs can be scaled on the elevation sheet or wall section. Order the next even foot length of lumber. Then add two studs for every opening. The length of these opening studs will be the same as the stud height for each story.

RIBBON FOR BALLOON FRAMING

A ribbon (riband) is a piece of 1″ stock notched into the inside face of studs which are two stories in height and form a support for the second floor joists. See figure

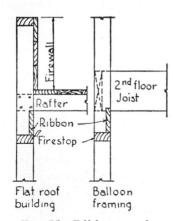

Flat roof building

Balloon framing

FIG. 23—*Ribbons and Firestops*

23. Ribbon material is sometimes used on one-story flat-roofed houses. In this case the studs are long enough to form the firewall of the roof. The width of the ribbon will vary according to the plans and building ordinances. 1" x 4" and 1" x 6" are commonly used.

Rule: Order as many linear feet of ribbon stock as there are linear feet of outside supporting walls. The direction of the second floor or ceiling joists will determine which are supporting walls as any wall parallel to the joists does not require a ribbon.

FIRESTOPS IN BALLOON FRAMING

Additional firestops are needed in an outside wall to close up the space behind the ribbon and behind the outside end joists. The size is the same as the studs.

Rule: Perimeter of the building equals linear feet of firestop material.

COVE BRACKETS

Cove brackets are required in any room that has a cove ceiling. Each bracket is made of 2" rough lumber bandsawed to the radius given on the plans, and nailed in the angle formed by a stud and ceiling joist. See figure 20, page 48.

Rule: Multiply the perimeter of the room by ¾; then add two extra brackets to allow for framing situations in which the studs may be closer than 16″ o.c. Allow one hip cove for each corner or angle. Repeat for all coved ceiling rooms. (The lath can be curved to fit the angle and no hip coves used.)

Fig. 24—*Roof Sheathing and Firewall*

STORM SHEATHING

Storm sheathing, sometimes called diagonal boarding, is 1″ x 6″ lumber, cut and nailed on the outside of exterior framed walls. It is also necessary on the inside face of firewall studs. It is laid either straight or at a 45 degree angle. See figure 24. There are four framing situations to be considered; walls without openings, walls with openings, gables, and firewall areas. The manner of laying it affects the quantity of material as there is more waste when laying it diagonally.

Rule for walls without openings: Multiply the wall height, from sill line to top plate, by the building perimeter. If sheathing is laid straight add $\frac{1}{10}$; if laid diagonally add $\frac{1}{6}$. Result equals board feet of sheathing required.

Rule for walls with openings: Laid straight: Find the total wall area (as above), deduct all openings 20 sq. ft. or more. Result equals board feet of sheathing.

Laid diagonally: Find the total wall area; deduct all openings 20 sq. ft. or more; then add $\frac{1}{10}$. Result equals board feet of sheathing.

Rule for gable area: Find gable area by multiplying roof rise by one half the span. If sheathing is laid straight add $\frac{1}{10}$; if laid diagonally add $\frac{1}{5}$.

FIRE WALL SHEATHING

Firewall sheathing is required on flat-roof houses when the outside walls project above the line of the roof. See figure 24. The sheathing is laid horizontally or sometimes follows the slope of a roof. There is considearble waste due to this slope which is allowed for by using the firewall dimension as measured at the lowest part of the roof.

Rule: Multiply the roof perimeter by the height of the fire wall at the lowest part of the roof. Result equals board feet of sheathing.

WALL SHEATHING FOR SHINGLES

Shingle lath or sheathing is 1″ x 3″ or 1″ x 4″ laid horizontally on the outside face of wall studs to form a nailing surface for wood shingles. See figure 21 page 49.

The spacing of sheathing varies. One trade practice is to space the sheathing from center to center twice the shingle exposure. The following table covers this situation.

NOTE: In good construction building paper is nailed on the exterior face of the studs before the framing or finish lumber is put on. This method of construction helps to insulate the building. See page 43 for rule to use when estimating the paper.

TABLE X
SHINGLE SHEATHING TABLE

Spacing Center to Center	8″	9″	10″
Constant for 1″ x 3″	.4	.35	.3
Constant for 1″ x 4″	.6	.5	.45

Rule: Figure total area to be covered. Deduct area of all openings. Multiply net area by constant selected on basis of shingle exposure. Add 5% to allow for waste. Result equals board feet of sheathing required.

PLASTER GROUNDS FOR BASEBOARD

Plaster grounds are not really a part of the frame-work of a building but

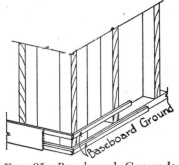

FIG. 25—*Baseboard Grounds*

are considered in this unit so as not to be overlooked. They are strips of lumber ⅞″ x ⅞″, or of a thickness to match the plasterer's work, nailed horizontally on the inside face of studs a little below the top of the finish base. See figure 25. They serve as a guide for the plasterer so that a true and straight plastered surface can be obtained. The exact size of the ground is determined by specification or building ordinance requirements.

> *Rule*: Figure the perimeter of each room, then deduct the width of each door or archway opening. Result equals linear feet of ground stock. Opening widths are reduced to the nearest foot.

Note: Trade practice in some areas permits nailing on baseboard *before* plastering. A piece of 1″ x 4″ flooring stock is often used. The base then becomes a ground for the plaster. To protect base it is painted on all surfaces before plastering is done.

CEILING UNIT

The ceiling unit divides itself into three parts: ceiling joists, stiffeners, or strongbacks, and backing.

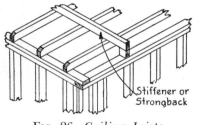

Fig. 26—*Ceiling Joists and Stiffener*

CEILING JOISTS

Ceiling joists are placed horizontally on top of walls and partitions forming the framework of a ceiling. See figure 26. The direction in which they run is based on the shape of a roof, as ceiling joists act as a tie to keep a building from spreading. It is an advantage to have them run the short way of a room so as to decrease the span, making the joists less likely to sag. For all plastered interiors joists are spaced 16″ on centers (o.c.).

> *Rule*: Multiply the length of the supporting wall or partition by ¾; then add 1. Length of joist equals distance between two partitions opposite walls or plus at least 8″ to provide a good bearing. Then increase to a standard length of lumber.

CEILING BACKING

Backing is needed on the top plate of all partitions that run parallel to the ceiling joists. These are called cross partitions. Extra ceiling joists are used for backing. See figure 27. The length of backing is determined by the length of a partition.

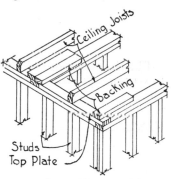

FIG. 27—*Ceiling Backing*

> *Rule*: Allow two extra ceiling joists for each cross partition. Scale length of partition; then add at least 8″ to provide a bearing for each end of the joist. Increase to a standard length of lumber.

STIFFENERS

A stiffener, or strong back, is a piece of framing lumber nailed at right angles to and on top of ceiling joists. It is placed at the center of a span to stiffen the joists. See figure 26. Ordinary size rooms require one piece; larger rooms require two pieces. The plans, specifications and building ordinances are governing factors. The length of a stiffener is determined by room dimensions.

> *Rule*: Allow one piece for each main room of a house, and one extra piece for each large room. The length or width dimension of the room plus at least 8″ equals the length of the piece. Increase to a standard length of lumber.

ROOF UNIT

The framing members of a roof are rafters, ridge, sheathing, gable studs, braces, and filler.

Rafters are pieces of lumber framed to form the slope or pitch of a roof. See figure 28. The number and length vary with the roof shape and pitch. Lengths of the different rafters can be figured mathematically, graphically, scaled on the blueprint, or by using a carpenter's steel square.

FIG. 28—*Common Rafters*

Sheathing is material placed at right angle to and on top of the rafters to form a surface for the roofing. A ridge board is used at the top end of rafters to form a continuous tie while the roof is being raised. Braces, which vary in number and length according to the slope and span of a roof, are placed under the rafters to stiffen them. Gable studs are used to construct the framework of a wall formed by a pair of rafters placed at the end of a building. See figure 29. The filler is framing lumber placed at the plate line between each rafter to close the space between the top plate and the sheathing. See figure 30.

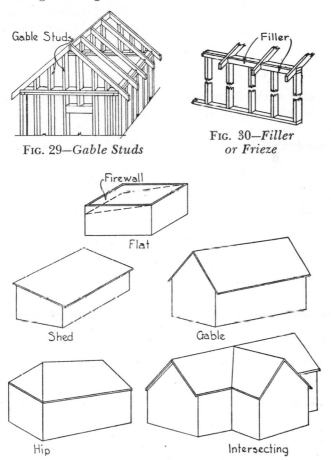

FIG. 29—*Gable Studs*

FIG. 30—*Filler or Frieze*

FIG. 31—*Types of Roofs*

TYPES OF ROOFS

A shed roof is the simplest type, the slant being in one direction only. A gable roof has a slant in two opposite directions. A hip roof slants in four directions while an intersecting roof is a combination of these types and is needed for a building which has an L or offset. See figure 31.

WHAT PITCH IS*

Pitch is the term used to denote the mathematcial relationship between the slope and span of a roof. Its use enables an architect to quickly indicate what the ridge height is to be above the plate line. For a building 32' wide with a ¼ pitch roof the ridge is 8' above the plate. A half pitch roof with a span of 40' would have the ridge 20' above the plate.

Rule: Pitch times span gives the ridge height.

MATHEMATICAL RELATIONSHIP BETWEEN FLOOR AND ROOF AREAS

There is a definite mathematical relationship between the floor and roof area of a building, this relationship varying with the pitch. An estimator's take-off problems are greatly simplified by using a series of constants to find roof areas or common rafter lengths.

In the following table the contants given indicate how much the roof area is increased over the floor area.

To illustrate: A building is 32' x 40' in size. The roof-pitch is ⅓. What is roof area?

---

*For a detailed description of the mathematical principles of a roof and how to lay out different rafters, see *Simplified Roof Framing* by Wilson and Werner. McGraw-Hill Book Co., New York.

TABLE XI

CONSTANT TABLE FOR COMMON RAFTER LENGTHS AND ROOF AREAS WHEN ROOF IS EQUAL PITCH

Pitch	Cut	Constant
1/8	3 & 12	1.03
1/6	4 & 12	1.05
5/24	5 & 12	1.08
1/4	6 & 12	1.12
7/24	7 & 12	1.16
1/3	8 & 12	1.20
3/8	9 & 12	1.25
5/12	10 & 12	1.30
1/2	12 & 12	1.41
7/12	14 & 12	1.54
5/8	15 & 12	1.60
2/3	16 & 12	1.67
3/4	18 & 12	1.80
5/6	20 & 12	1.95
11/12	22 & 12	2.09
FULL	24 & 12	2.24
13/12	26 & 12	2.39
7/6	28 & 12	2.54
5/4	30 & 12	2.70
4/3	32 & 12	2.85
17/12	34 & 12	3.01
3/2	36 & 12	3.17
19/12	38 & 12	3.33
5/3	40 & 12	3.48

Solution: 32' x 40' equals 1280 square feet of floor area. The constant for a 1/3 pitch roof is 1.20. 1280 x 1.20 equals 1536 square feet which is the roof area.

The same principle can be applied to find common rafter lengths.

To illustrate: What is the length of lumber to order for common rafters for a building with a 36' span and a ¼ pitch roof?

Solution: 36' of span equal 18' of rafter run. The constant for a ¼ pitch roof is 1.12. Then 18' times 1.12 equals 20.16 which is increased to a 22' length of lumber.

Rule to find roof area: Use the constant table and multiply floor area by the constant given for the required pitch. Result equals roof area, sometimes called pitch area. If the roof has a cornice, increase building dimensions by twice the cornice run and then find the floor and cornice area combined. Then multiply by the constant.

Rule to find common rafter length: Multiply rafter run (one half the roof span) by the constant given for the required pitch. Result equals rafter length. If roof has a cornice, overhang length must be added to this result. Then increase to a standard length of lumber.

NOTE: This method of finding rafter lengths is a very practical one for the estimator but is not easily adaptable for the carpenter on the job. He usually lays out rafter lengths and cuts by using his steel square.

KINDS OF RAFTERS

There are four kinds of rafters listed by an estimator when taking off a bill of materials for a roof. The most common is the common rafter, hence its name. This rafter is required for all types of roofs. Hip rafters form the frame work at the corner or hip of a hipped roof. Valley rafters are used at the 90 degree intersection of the two (or more) parts of an intersecting roof.

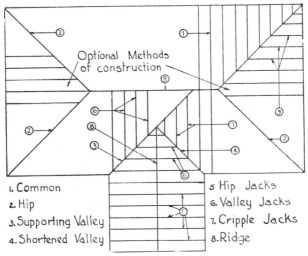

FIG. 32— *Illustrating Various Rafters*

1. Common
2. Hip
3. Supporting Valley
4. Shortened Valley
5. Hip Jacks
6. Valley Jacks
7. Cripple Jacks
8. Ridge

Jack rafters are required when hip or valley rafters are used. See figure 32.

LENGTH OF COMMON RAFTER

The length of any rafter is, mathematically, the hypotenuse of a right angle triangle. For the common rafter the rafter run is the base of the triangle and the roof or rafter rise is the altitude. See figure 33. The estimator's problem is to find the hypotenuse of this triangle. This can be done in several ways.

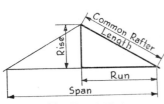

FIG. 33—*Roof Terms*

Rule 1: The simplest method is to use an architect's scale and read the length of the rafter on a blueprint. This method can only be used for the common rafter.

Rule 2: A second way is to use a table and multiply the rafter run by a constant given for a definite pitch. See table XI, page 61.

NUMBER OF COMMON RAFTERS

Rule: To find the number of common rafters multiply plate length on which the rafters are to be nailed by the rafter spacing constant. See table VII, page 32. Part of a space must be counted as a full one. Then add one. This gives the number of one side of a gable roof. Double result for the other side.

LENGTH OF HIP OR VALLEY RAFTER FOR EQUAL PITCH ROOF

The length of a hip or valley rafter can be found mathematically by multiplying the span by a constant which is different for each pitch. These constants are given in table XII.

Rule 1: Span times a constant selected for the required pitch equals length of hip or valley rafter for an equal pitch roof. Increase to a standard length of lumber when ordering.

Rule 2: The diagonal of one half the span and the common rafter length will also give the length of a hip or valley rafter for an equal pitch roof. See

TABLE XII

CONSTANT TABLE FOR HIP AND VALLEY RAFTER LENGTHS ON EQUAL PITCH ROOFS

Pitch	Cut	Constant
1/8	3 & 12	.72
1/6	4 & 12	.73
5/24	5 & 12	.74
1/4	6 & 12	.75
7/24	7 & 12	.77
1/3	8 & 12	.78
3/8	9 & 12	.80
5/12	10 & 12	.82
1/2	12 & 12	.87
7/12	14 & 12	.92
5/8	15 & 12	.94
2/3	16 & 12	.97
3/4	18 & 12	1.03
5/6	20 & 12	1.09
11/12	22 & 12	1.16
FULL	24 & 12	1.23
13/12	26 & 12	1.29
7/6	28 & 12	1.36
5/4	30 & 12	1.44
4/3	32 & 12	1.51
17/12	34 & 12	1.53
3/2	36 & 12	1.66
19/12	38 & 12	1.73
5/3	40 & 12	1.81

figure 34. This can quickly be established by using a carpenter's steel square.

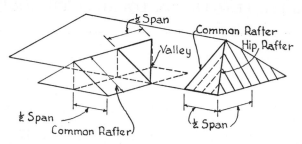

FIG. 34—*Basic Principle Involved When Finding Length of Hip or Valley Rafter for an Equal Pitch Roof*

LENGTH OF HIP OR VALLEY RAFTER FOR UNEQUAL PITCH ROOF*

An unequal pitch roof results when a building has a wing which is narrower than the main part of the building, but a ridge height which is the same for both parts of the roof. See figure 35.

The length of an unequal pitch valley can be figured on the basis of either of two angles. One angle is formed by using the length of the common rafter of the *major* span and one half the *minor* span measurements; the other angle is formed by using the length of the common rafter of the *minor* span and one half of the *major* span measurement.

*See Chap. V, *Simplified Roof Framing*, Wilson and Werner, McGraw-Hill Book Co.

To illustrate: How long will a valley rafter be for a roof that has a major span of 40′ and a wing or minor span of 18′? The roof pitch is ⅜. Ridge height is the same for both parts.

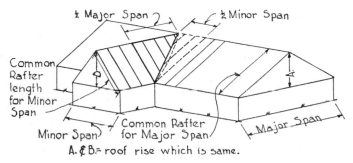

Fig. 35—*Illustrating Angles Involved When Finding Length of Unequal Pitch Valley Rafter*

Solution: Ridge height is ⅜ times 40′ (major span) or 15′. The minor span common rafter run is 9′ (one half of 18′). The diagonal of rafter run (9′) and roof rise (15′) is 17′-6″ which is common rafter length of the minor span.

To find the valley rafter length, use the measurements as found above 17′-6″ (common rafter length) and 20′-0″ (one half major span) and measure the hypotenuse of the angle. This will be 26′-6″ and is increased to a 28′ piece of lumber. A study of figure 35 will indicate that either angle could have been used (that is the one shown by the heavy lines or the one shown by dotted lines). The hypotenuse is the same in both cases.

Rule: The hypotenuse of one half the major span and the length of the common rafter of the minor span equals the length of the valley rafter. If the building has a cornice, the cornice run must be added to the span measurement and the angle figured on the increased measurement.

NUMBER OF HIP OR VALLEY RAFTERS

Rule: Number of pieces: Allow one piece of lumber for each hip and one piece for each valley in a roof. The size of stock will vary. Hips and valleys are usually 2″ wider than common rafter stock.

NUMBER OF HIP OR VALLEY JACK RAFTERS

A hip roof has exactly the same area as a gable roof assuming the building dimensions and ratfer pitch are the same. The number of pieces of rafter stock to make the jacks will be the same as if common rafters were ordered. Tip and valley rafters will have to be estimated separately.

Rule 1: *Figure a hip roof as though it were a gable roof.*

Rule 2: If the roof is an intersecting one, figure the main roof as though it were a gable roof; repeat for the smaller roof; in other words, figure each wing separately. Common rafter stock will cut up into jacks without waste if the carpenter is careful. The piece off the longest jack will be long enough for the shortest jack, etc.

Rule 3: For a roof with a cornice, add cornice run to building dimensions and proceed as outlined above.

To illustrate above rules: List the jack rafters for the hip roof shown in figure 36. Pitch is 1/4. Common rafter spacing is 24″ on centers.

Solution: The length of the common rafter for this roof is the diagonal of ½ the span (10′) and the ridge height (5′). This is 11′-2⅛″, requiring a 12′ piece of lumber.

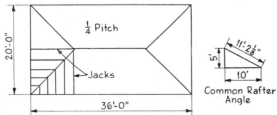

Fig. 36—*A Practical Jack Rafter Problem*

Number of rafters: 36 x ½ (24″ o.c.) equals 18. 18 plus 1 equals 19 rafters for one side or 38 pieces for both sides. Therefore order 38 pieces 2 x 4- or 2 x 6-12′ which will be sufficient to make all common and jack rafters in the roof. In addition, there will have to be 4 pieces of stock to make the hips. The length of these will be 20′ (span) x .751 or 15.02 and called 16′-0″. (See hip constant table XII, page 65.)

SUMMARY OF RAFTER LENGTH RULES

1. Pitch times span equals total rise.

2. Diagonal of ½ the span and the rise equals common rafter length.

3. Jack rafters are figured as though the roof were gable type.

4. Diagonal of ½ the span and common rafter length equals the length of a hip or valley.

5. Diagonal of common rafter length of minor span and one half the major span (or vice versa) equals

length of unequal pitch valley rafter. Use the same principle for an unequal hip rafter.

COMPOSITION ROOF SHEATHING

The amount of roof sheathing required depends on the kind of roofing material specified. If composition roofing is used the sheathing problem is identical with sub-floor estimating as 1″ x 6″ stock S1S1E is most generally used. Sometimes specifications call for it to be laid diagonally. On most residential work roof sheathing is laid straight.

Rule: To find board feet of sheathing stock:

a. Figure the plan area of a roof. Plan area is found by multiplying the width and length building dimensions together and subtracting the "take-away" areas. See figure 17, page 24.

   If there is a cornice add run to the building dimensions before multiplying together.

b. Multiply this plan area by a constant from table XI, page 61. selected according to roof pitch. Result equals roof or pitch area.

c. Multiply this roof area by a constant from table XIII selected according to the way the material is milled and laid.

TABLE XIII
CONSTANT TABLE FOR SOLID
ROOF-SHEATHING

How Laid	1 x 6		1 x 6 S1S1E to 5½″	
Size of Stock	Straight	Diagonal	Straight	Diagonal
Constant	1.10	1.16	1.2	1.26

WOOD SHINGLE SHEATHING

Rule: If wood shingles are specified, proceed as above and find the pitch area. If 4″ sheathing is used laid 8 ″or 9″ on center, multiply roof area by ½; then add 5%. If 6″ sheathing, multiply by ⅔; then add 5%.

SUMMARY OF ROOF AREA RULES

Shed Roof: Rafter length times ridge length equals roof area.

Gable Roof: Rafter length times ridge length multiplied by two equals roof area.

Hip Roof: Common rafter length times building length multiplied by two equals roof area.

Gambrel Roof: Rafter length of each part of the roof times building length equals roof area. Combine all areas.

Intersecting Roof (also Hip Roof): Floor area multiplied by correct decimal increase equals roof area. See table XI, page 61. If the building has a cornice, the plan area of the roof must be estimated. To find plan area, add the horizontal roof projection measurements to the floor plan measurement, then multiply the width by the length.

ROOF RIDGE

The length of a ridge is determined on a blueprint by using a scale rule and reading the length as drawn on the elevation sheet or roof plan. Increase to an even foot length of lumber.

Rule: If the building has a gable roof the length of the ridge equals either the width or length dimensions of the building. If the building has a hip roof the ridge length equals the difference between the width and length measurements. If the building has an intersecting roof the length should be scaled on the blueprint. See figure 32, page 63.

GABLE STUDS

Gable studs are usually spaced 16″ o.c. and placed, if possible directly over the wall studs. See figure 29, page 59.

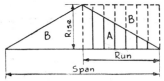

RISE × RUN = GABLE AREA

FIG. 37—*Method of Figuring Gable Studs*

Rule: The length of each stud is considered to be the same as the distance between the ridge and the plate line. To find the number of studs multiply one half the span distance by ¾. Figuring one half the area, but considering each stud to be as long as the center one will give enough stock for the entire gable. See figure 37.

BRACES (OR TRUSSES)

Braces for a roof are difficult to estimate as the amount needed varies according to the length of the rafters. A short rafter needs no center support. If a 2″ x 4″ rafter is inclined to be "springy" because of its length sometimes a 2″ x 6″ rafter is used.

Rule for Purline: If one horizontal support is needed under the rafters twice the length of the building equals linear feet required. This piece is called a purline.

Rule for Posts: To find the number of posts to support the purline multiply the linear feet of purline by ⅓. This will provide a post every 4'. The length of these posts can be scaled on the blueprint measuring on the gable end of the roof.

FILLER

Lumber used to close up the spaces over the top plate line is usually 2″ framing stock if the exterior walls are to be plastered. See figure 30, page 59. When siding is used the top siding board is often fitted around each rafter. Occasionally a finished piece of lumber, called frieze, is used and fitted between the rafters.

Rule: The linear feet of all exterior walls that support the rafters equals the linear feet of filler (or frieze stock).

STAIR UNIT*

A special piece of framing material called a stair horse is required to which stair treads are nailed. There is usually sufficient rough stock on the job to make temporary stair treads.

STAIR HORSES

A stair horse is rough stock either cut or built up to form supports for the steps and risers of a stairway.

*See page 264.

See figure 38. An ordinary stairway requires three horses. The size of the material is given on the detail sheet or in the specifications.

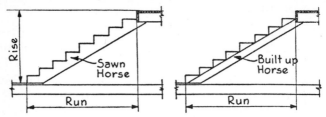

FIG. 38—*Built-Up or Sawn Stair Horses*

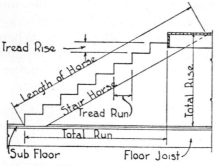

FIG. 39—*Rise and Run of a Stairway*

Rule: The diagonal distance of total run and total rise of a stairway will give the approximate length of a stair horse. The total rise equals the vertical distance from finished floor to the finished floor above. Total run is the horizontal distance over which the stair horse "runs." See figure 39. Use a steel square to find the diagonal of this angle or measure the distance by laying out a right angle using rise and run measurements.

CHAPTER IV

EXTERIOR FINISH

AFTER A HOUSE is framed there is considerable work to be done closing in the frame and the openings. This work varies according to the kind of finish the exterior walls are to have. On many houses siding is used; occasionally an architect will specify shingles.

Fig. 40—*Typical Window Frames*

The estimating work is divided into four units as follows: window and door frames, walls, cornice, and roofing. Each unit includes several kinds of materials.

FRAME UNIT

MILL MADE FRAMES

A window or door frame is a complete unit, constructed of finished material into which a window or exterior door is fitted and hung. Figure 40 indicates some typical frames.

The carpenter sometimes constructs frames on the job as shown in figure 41 or frames may be purchased from a mill, some of which specialize in this type of of work.

FIG. 41—*Making Window Frames 'on the Job'*

The frames are "set" at varying stages of erection, depending upon the exterior construction. For a plastered exterior, they are set before the outside lathing is done. In the West frames are set after the siding is on; in the East, they are set after the storm sheathing is on, but before the finish siding is fitted and nailed.

WINDOW AND DOOR FRAMES

To list a group of windows or door frames requires that many items of information be given.

Number of Frames: This means the quantity of frames required, and only those frames that are alike in every detail may be grouped.

Name of Frame: The name is derived from the kind of window, sash or door fitted into the frame. The common types are:

    a. Double hung window, slides vertically.

    b. Casement window, swings in or out.

    c. Stationary window, does not open.

    d. Door, opens in or out.

For any type of frame that has two or more openings, the sash can be double hung, casement, stationary or a combination of any of these three. When a frame is constructed to take care of two separate windows, it is known as a mullion frame (see figure 42); if for three windows it is called a triplet frame. (See figure 43.) The term mullion casing is applied to the vertical trim that separate a frame into two or more parts.

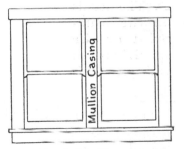

Fig. 42—*A Mullion Double Hung Window Frame*

Size of Frame: The dimensions of a frame are listed the same as the size of the window, sash or doors for which the frame is made. The width is given first and then the length. To illustrate: A frame for a 2'-3" x 3'-0" window would be ordered: one double hung window frame 2'-3" x 3'-0". To order a triplet frame the procedure varies slightly. For example: The plans show two casement sash 2'-0" x 4'-6" and one stationary sash 4'-0" x 4"-6' to go into one frame. The order would be listed as one $\dfrac{2'\text{-}0'' \ \text{x} \ 4'\text{-}0'' \ \text{x} \ 2'\text{-}0''}{4''\text{-}6''}$ triplet window frame.

The expression $\dfrac{2'\text{-}0'' \ \text{x} \ 4'\text{-}0'' \ \text{x} \ 2'\text{-}0''}{4'\text{-}6''}$ means that the outside windows are 2'-0" wide; the center sash 4'-0" wide and all are 4'-6" long. See figure 43.

Thickness of the Jamb: The thickness of the jamb stock will vary from 1" to 2". The details on the blueprint or the specifications will give this information.

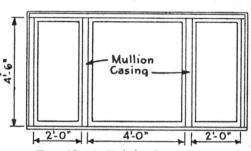

Fig. 43—*A Triple Casement Window Frame*

Width of the Jamb or Pulley Stile Stocks The measurement is very important as a frame is usually set in place before the inside wall is plastered and must project beyond the face of the studding to provide the corretc thickness for inferior plaster. The thickness of the exterior finish must be figured likewise. The exact width of the jamb stock is based on an architect's detail. Sometimes it may be determined by adding the thickness of the outside finish, the width of the wall studs, and the thickness desired for finish material on the inside face of the wall. Figure 44 indicates the relation of these parts.

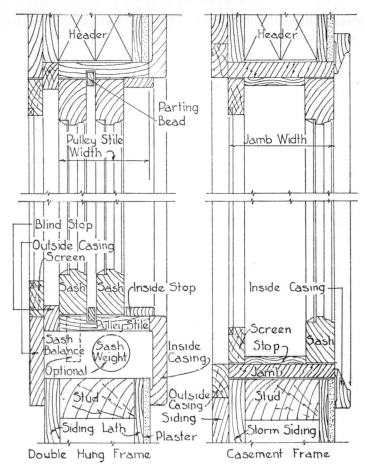

Header

Parting
Bead

Pulley Stile
Width

Jamb Width

Blind Stop
Outside Casing
Screen

Sash Sash Inside Stop

Pulley Stile

Sash
Balance

Sash
Weight

Optional

Inside
Casing

Stud

Siding Lath

Inside Casing

Screen
Stop

Sash

Jamb

Stud

Outside
Casing
Siding

Plaster

Storm Siding

Double Hung Frame

Casement Frame

FIG. 44—*The Different Parts of Casement and
Double Hung Window Frames*

Kind of lumber used for Jambs This will vary according to the specifications for the building and the location

of a frame in a building. Douglas fir and cypress are
often used for this purpose.

*Construction of the Case-
ment Jamb or Door Jamb*:
There are two ways of making
a jamb for a door or casement
frame as shown in figure 45.
(a) The stop is nailed on; or
(b) the jamb is made of a thick
piece of stock and rabbetted to
suit the thickness of the sash or
door. An outside door jamb is
similar to a casement window
jamb except for size of rabbett and the kind of lumber
used for sill.

Fig. 45—*Two Methods
of Making a Casement
Jamb or Door Jamb*

The jamb for a double hung window frame is called
a pulley stile, see figure 44, and requires a piece of
blind stop and parting bead to complete it. The blind
stop gets its name from the fact it provides a stop for
the outside blind or shutter. If a blind is not used, it
serves the same purpose for the window screen. The
parting bead serves as a guide and separates or parts
the upper and lower vertical sliding sash.

Thickness of the Sash or Door: This measurement
is very important, as the jamb for a frame cannot be
milled until this is known. If a double hung frame, the
pulley stile must be grooved to fit the thickness of the
window. For a casement sash or door the jamb must be
rabbetted the same as the thickness of the sash or door.

Which Way the Casement Sash or Door Opens: A
casement sash, or outside door, may open in or out and
the correct information must be stated on the order.

Size of Outside Casings: The measurement is given on the plans or in the specifications.

Kind of Lumber for Outside Casings: Redwood is often used for this purpose due to its weather resisting qualities. However, the specifications should be consulted.

Size of the Sill: The size of the sill is shown on the detail sheet, or will be given in the specifications.

Kind of Lumber for Sill: Redwood is often used for window sills. Door frame sills are usually vertical grained Douglas fir or oak. This information is given in the specifications.

Shape of Sill: The plans will usually have a detail of the sill for a frame. If none is given, the mill will use a standard pattern.

Width of the Mullion Casing: A mullion casing is the vertical casing between any two sash fastened in the same window frame, as shown in figure 42, page 77. It is not always the same width for every frame on a job. The detail sheet will usually give the width of the mullion casing The kind of lumber is the same as the outside casing (see above).

JOB MADE FRAMES

On some jobs window and door frames are made by the carpenter. It is then necessary to estimate the different materials needed such as jambs, pulley stiles, outside casings, band moulding, blind stop, parting bead and sills. See figure 44.

The two side jambs and the top piece (head) of a frame are the same shape and kind of material. The sill is always a different shape and size than the side and head jambs.

The frame size is the same as the door or window for which it is made, hence these sizes are used as the basis for figuring lengths of stock needed to make a frame.

Material for mullion jambs is often the same size and shape as the stock used for the balance of the frame. If the specifications or detail drawings indicate a different shaped piece, a separate list of material must be made.

CASEMENT WINDOW JAMBS

A casement jamb is that part of a casement window frame into which the sash is fitted and hung. The vertical pieces are known as side jambs; the horizontal piece at the top of the frame is called the head jamb. The sill at the bottom of the frame is not the same shape material and must be figured separately.

The width of jamb stock will depend on the width of the studs and the thickness of the finish on each face of the wall. Blueprints will usually give exact details and specifications will state the thickness of the lumber.

Rule: To find the length of a casement jamb, multiply the length of the window by two; add the width of the window; allow 12″ more for joints; then increase to the next even foot length of stock. One piece of jamb stock is required for each casement window.*

If the frame is a mullion or triplet, figure each opening separately.

*See table on page 163.

NOTE: There are two ways of constructing a mullion or triplet frame. One way is to construct the frame with a continuous head jamb, the mullion side jambs being "gained" into it. The second method is to construct the frame by making each opening in it a separate one; this method requiring two side jambs and one head jamb for each window. The sill is always continuous for all mullion and triplet frames. See figure 46. The window jamb rule given above applies to the second situation.

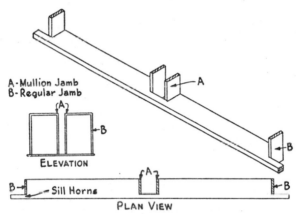

FIG. 46—*Mullion Jambs and Window Sill*

OUTSIDE DOOR JAMBS

The jamb is that part of a frame into which a door is fitted and hung. A door frame requires one piece of stock to make the two sides and head jamb.

The width of the stock used is determined by the type of construction. The width of the stud plus the thickness of material on each face of the framed wall, equals the exact width of the finished jamb. Specifications will state thickness of jambs. If the wall is not standard construction an architect usually draws a special detail.

>*Rule*: The length of the jamb stock is computed as
>   follows: Twice the door length plus door width
>   plus 12″. Then increase to a standard length of
>   lumber.

PULLEY STYLE

Pulley stile is that part of a double hung window frame into which a window is fitted and hung. It is made with a ⅜″ groove near the center into which the parting bead is fitted. This bead separates the upper and lower sash of a window. Two pulleys are fitted into each stile, near the top end, hence the same pulley stile. Sash balances are sometimes used in place of pulleys but the term "pulley-stile" still applies.

If the width of the pulley stile is not given on the detail sheet, determine exact width of the finished wall. This will be stud width plus thickness of lath and plaster on the interior, plus thickness of exterior finish. Then subtract the thickness of the blind stop, usually ¾″. See figure 44, page 79. This will give the width of the pulley stile. The standard thickness of the stile is 1³⁄₁₆″.

>*Rule*: Twice the length of a window, plus the width
>   of a window, plus 12″ equals required length.
>   Then increase to a standard length for lumber.
>   For mullion or triplet frames figure one piece for
>   each opening.

OUTSIDE CASINGS

Outside casing is finish stock nailed on the outside face of a door, double hung or casement window frame. It is usually redwood or other weather resisting material. The size of the casing is determined from the blueprint or specifications. The square joint is used at the corners.

Rule 1: For a single frame the rule is: Twice the length of the frame plus width of the frame plus 12"; then increase to a standard length of lumber.

Rule 2: If the frame is a mullion or triplet three steps are necessary to find the length of the casing stock.

   a. Side casings: Multiply the length of the frame by two.

   b. Head casings: Add width of all sash in the frame; then add width of all casings.

   c. Now combine lengths found in "a" and "b" into standard lengths of lumber which will cut with the least waste.

NOTE: It is advisable to indicate on the lumber bill how these pieces are to be cut. The carpenter can then quickly select the correct lengths which have been ordered for each frame.

Rule 3: Mullion casings are ordered as follows: The width may be different than the regular casing. Length of frame plus 2" equals length of one mullion casing. Multiply result by the number of mullions or combine into standard lengths of lumber.

PLASTER MOULDING

On buildings with plastered exteriors the flat casing on a window or door frame is often omitted and a small moulding substituted. The size of this moulding will vary according to the exterior construction and the architect's detail. A stock size is 2″ x 2″. Plaster moulding is usually not required on mullion jambs.

Rule 1: Twice the frame length plus the width plus 6″ equals the required length. Increase to a standard length of moulding.

Rule 2: If mullion casing mouldings are specified double length of each mullion casing; then add 4″ for joints. Repeat for each casing. Order one length of moulding for each mullion or combine into lengths which will cut with the least waste.

BLIND STOPS

Blind stops is a piece of surfaced stock nailed to one edge of a pulley stile and serves a two-fold purpose. Formerly it served as a stop for a shutter or blind which used to be hung on the exterior of many windows frames; hence its name. The hinged screen has taken the place of the blind, so the blind stop is now a screen stop. It also serves as a guide for the top sash of the double hung window. See figure 44, page 79.

A standard size of blind stop is ¾″ x 1½″. It is made of redwood or some other weather resisting wood.

Rule: Add twice the window length to the window width; allow 6″ more for joints; then increase to a standard length of stock. Each opening in a mullion or triplet frame is figured separtely and requires one piece of blind stop.

PARTING BEAD

Parting bead, see figure 44, page 79, is a small piece of ⅜" x ¾" stock with two rounded edges fitted into the groove of a pulley stile and separates or "parts" the upper and lower sash of a double hung window.

> *Rule*: Twice the length of a window plus its width, plus 6", then increase to a standard length of stock. Each window in a mullion or triplet frame is figured separately; therefore, allow one piece of parting bead for each opening in a frame.

DOOR AND WINDOW SILLS

A door or window sill forms the bottom end of a window or door frame and is placed in a sloping position to permit rain water to run outward.

The width of a sill will vary according to the thickness of the framed wall. There is also a projection to allow for as a sill projects beyond the face of casing stock, usually 1". The standard thickness of sill stock is 1¾". The shape will generally be detailed on a blueprint; if not, a stock pattern is carried by the mill.

Lumber used for window frame sills is redwood or other weather resisting material. For door sills, a vertical grained piece of Douglass fir or a piece of hardwood, such as oak, is used. The hardwood sill is generally used on a front door frame.

The length of the sill horns, see figure 46, page 83, affects the length of stock required to make a sill. On frames that have a 4½" or 5½" casing 12" should be allowed. For frames that have narrow trim, or only a band moulding, 6" is sufficient.

Rule: For a single frame, from 6″ to 12″ should be
added to the width of the frame to get the sill
length. For a mullion frame, see figure 42, page 77,
add the combined width of the sash to the combined width of the mullion casings, then add 6″
to 12″ and increase to a standard length of lumber.
Combine several sills to make a standard length.

WALL UNIT*

The materials considered in this unit are siding,
shingles, water table, belt course, and corner boards.

SIDING

Siding is finish lumber nailed horizontally on the
exterior of a frame building. Sometimes it is called

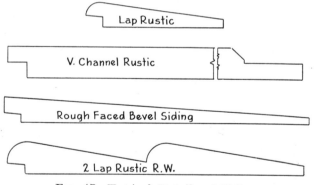

Fig. 47—*Typical Details of Siding*

rustic, channel rustic, beveled siding, novelty siding,
etc., each term being applied to some special shape of
material. Figure 47 shows some of the more commonly
used patterns.

*See note about building paper on page 55.

A piece of siding will not lay or cover as much space as is indicated by its size. A 1″ x 8″ board will cover 7″ of space, a 1″ x 10″ covers 9″. This is because the rabbett in the bottom edge of siding laps over the board below it. This rabbett will average ½″ in width. Another ⅜″ is lost in making a rough piece of lumber into siding. A third factor is shrinkage, as a rough piece of lumber will shrink from ⅛″ to ¼″. There is also considerable end waste caused by cutting siding to join on the studs. A certain fractional part must, therefore, be added to the net area to allow for these losses.

It is necessary to know whether the wall surface is a solid one, without openings, or if it has window and door openings. Gable areas are considered as a solid surface, although occasionally there may be a small ventilator or louvre frame in a gable.

Rule for short walls: If the area to be covered is a small one, such as the side of a garage, then a convenient way is to figure the material by the piece, as follows: Divide the wall height by the amount one board covers. See figure 48. Result equals number of boards. Count part of a board as a whole one.

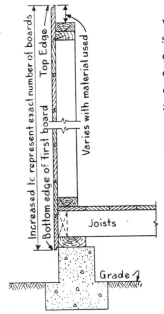

Fig. 48—*Wall Height to be Considered When Estimating Siding*

The length of the stock is the same as the length of the wall which must be considered in even foot lengths. Repeat for each short wall.

The following table indicates the amounts to add for various widths of siding. The explanation below the table shows the application of the table to walls without openings; gable areas and walls with openings.

TABLE XIV

SIDING TABLE

| Rough Lumber Size | Coverage | Waste | | Constant |
		Milling	End	
1 x 4	3″	33⅓%	5%	1.40*
1 x 6	5″	20%	5%	1.25
1 x 8	7″	15%	5%	1.20
1 x10	9″	12%	5%	1.17
1 x 12	11″	10%	5%	1.15

*Raised from 1.383 to 1.40 for convenience in using.

Rule to find wall area: Figure wall height by adding measurements from top of concrete to top of framed wall. Divide this result by "coverage" of one board. Increase to next whole number. This is number of boards required. Multiply by coverage of one board. Result equals *increased* wall height. See figure 48. The perimeter of the building equals the total wall length. Increased wall height times perimeter equals wall area.

Rule for a wall without openings: Find wall area and multiply by a constant selected from table XIV.

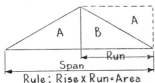

Rule: Rise × Run = Area

FIG. 49—*Method of Figuring Gable Area*

Rule for gable area: Multiply roof rise by one half the span, see figure 49. Then multiply this result by a constant selected from table XIV. Then add an additional 20% to allow for the waste incurred due to the slope of the roof. Result equals square feet of siding.

Rule for wall with openings: Find the wall area; deduct all openings 10 square feet in area, or more then multiply the remainder by a constant selected from table XIV.

SHINGLES ON WALLS

Occasionally a building will be designed with exterior walls to be covered with shingles.

Cedar, cypress and redwood lumber is used to make wood shingles due to their weather resisting qualities.

The thickness of the butt end of a shingle will vary, this thickness being stated in terms of the number of shingle butts that will measure 2″. To illustrate: shingles ordered 5/2 will measure five shingles to 2″; 6/2 means 6 shingles will measure 2″. Shingles are sold by the bundle, or "square" assuming 250 four-inch width shingles to a bundle.

When estimating shingles allowance must be made for door and window openings. Deduct all openings whose area is equal to or in excess of 10 square feet.*

*See table on page 166 for areas of different size openings.

Shingles will cover an identical amount of surface whether laid on a wall or a roof. The following table indicates the number of square feet of surface covered by one bundle of shingles for varying exposures and different length shingles.

TABLE XV
SHINGLE TABLE CONSTANTS*

Exposure	16″ Shingle	18″ Shingle	24″ Shingle
4	20	17½	
4½	22½	20	
5	25	22½	
5½	27½	25	
6	30	27½	20
6½	32½	30	22½
7	35		24
7½	37½		26½
8	40		

*Shingles are 16 , 18″ and 24″ long.

Rule: To find number of shingles for the exterior walls of a building:

  a. Figure the wall area by multiplying wall height by building perimeter.

  b. Figure gable areas by multiplying roof rise by rafter run. See figure 49.

  c. Combine results to get total wall area.

  d. Deduct combined area of all openings ten square feet or more in area.**

**See table on page 166.

e. Divide remainder by a constant selected from the shingle table based on shingle length and exposure.

Result equals number of bundles of shingles. Count a part of a bundle as a full one.

NOTE: Shingles are often sold by the "square." When figured on this basis the estimator must know how many bundles of shingles will cover one square (100 square feet). When shingles are used on exterior walls they are laid with a wider weather exposure than when laid on a roof; and therefore fewer bundles per square are required.

Rule 1: *Side-wall squares*: Divide the number of bundles by three. Result equals number of side wall squares, known as "three-bundle-squares."

Rule 2: *Roof-squares*: Divide number of bundles by four. Result equals number of roof-squares, known as "four-bundle-squares."

WATER TABLE

Water table is a piece of finish stock used for architectural effects at either the sill line of the house or at the same height as the sill line of the window frames. See figure 50.

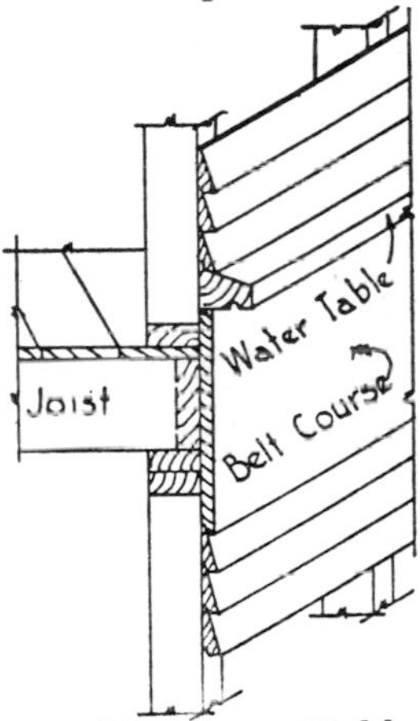

FIG. 50—*Water Table and Belt Course*

Rule: The perimeter of a building, plus 12″ for every outside corner (plus miters), equals the linear feet of water table required.

BELT COURSE

If an architect desires to make a break between a foundation and the exterior face of the outside walls, a continuous band known as a belt course is sometimes placed at the foundation sill line. Occasionally, a belt course will be placed at the second floor line of a two-story residence. See figure 50. The size of the stock used for this belt course will vary according to the architect's detail.

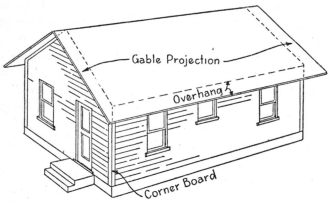

Fig. 51—*Illustrating Overhang and Gable Projections*

Rule: The perimeter of the building plus 12″ for every corner equals the number of linear feet of material to order.

CORNER BOARDS

Corner boards are pieces of finish stock sometimes required on exterior corners of a house finished with siding, as shown in figure 51. They provide certain architectural effects and also eliminate the necessity of making mitered joints on the siding. The size will be given on the blue print or in the specifications. One piece should always be 1″ wider than the other. The wide one is then lapped over the narrow one, so that both pieces appear to be of the same width. The kind of lumber is usually redwood or similar weather-resistant material.

> *Rule*: Allow two pieces of stock for every outside corner of the building. The length must be measured on the elevation sheets of the blueprint. Order one half the number required 1″ narrower than the finished width of the corner boards as shown on the blueprints.

CORNICE UNIT

The cornice is that part of a roof which extends beyond the outside walls of a house. There are two types, open and closed or box. In an open cornice the rafters and sheathing are exposed. In a closed or box cornice the rafters and sheathing are not seen and additional cornice material is required. The box cornice is always used on the colonial type of residence and is sometimes called a colonial cornice.

OPEN CORNICE

The open cornice is divided into two parts. See figure 51.

1. The overhang, the cornice which extends beyond the roof at the top plate line and forms the eaves of a roof.
2. The gable projection, that part of a roof which extends beyond the face of a gable wall.

The gable projection is often finished with a verge rafter which is supported by rafter lookouts or brackets. Sometimes only a moulding is used to form the finish. The cornice area is covered with various materials, one most commonly used being T&G ceiling stock.

VERGE RAFTERS

Verge rafters are pieces of finish lumber that form the finish of a gable end of a roof. The lumber is usually a better grade than used for rafters and generally S4S. The size is indicated on the elevation sheet or in the specifications.

> *Rule*: Count the verge rafters as shown on the elevation sheets. Each gable requires two. The length is the same as the common rafter and can be either measured on the elevation or figured mathematically using table XI, page 61.

NOTE: The same estimating rule will apply if a moulding is used instead of a verge rafter.

TONGUE AND GROOVE CEILING

Tongue and groove (T&G) 1″ x 6″ ceiling stock is often used to cover an open cornice in order that it may have a finished appearance. As a piece of 1″ x 6″ stock "lays" only 5¼″, additional stock must be ordered to have enough to cover a given surface.

Two rules are required to figure the area of a cornice. One applies to the overhang and the other to the gable projection.

> *Rule for overhang area*: Multiply the length of the rafter projection (in even feet or half feet) by the

length of the eave, which is building length plus gable projection. Shed or gable roofs have two overhang areas, one for each side wall. A hip roof will have four such areas, one for each outside wall. The eave length of a hip roof is building length (or width) plus twice the cornice run. Figure each of the four areas; then combine.

Rule for gable projection area:

a. To find the area of a gable projection for a shed roof multiply the rafter length, from plate line to ridge, by the distance the verge rafter is out from the building. For a gable roof compute the same way but double the result as there are two such areas in a gable.

b. Then ⅕ must be added to these areas to allow for some cornice boards to extend back to the second rafter to help prevent the verge rafter from sagging.

c. After the area is known then allowance must be made for loss due to milling and laying the T&G stock.

Rule for allowance for waste: Combine the gable projection area and the overhang area. Then add ⅙. The result equals square feet of T&G sheathing to order for an open cornice.

BOX CORNICE

A box cornice is composed of several parts, namely fascia, frieze, plancher, and moulding. See figure 52.

Rule: Check the detail sheets to find the sizes and number of parts to the box cornice. Use an architect's scale and measure the lengths of the cornice as shown on the different elevation sheets. Allow 12″ extra for each outside corner. Then order lengths that will cut with the least waste.

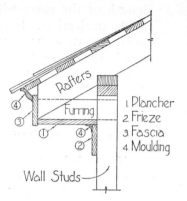

Fig. 52—*Section Through a Box Cornice*

ROOFING UNIT

The last unit of exterior finishing is roofing. There are a number of materials used, such as wood shingles, composition roofing (made as individual shingles, or in rolls), slate, tile, and metal.

Roofing is usually handled as a sub-contract in the same manner as plumbing, wiring, painting, etc.; therefore this section will include only a few of the materials.

The carpenter estimator should have catalogues on file which describes in detail the various roofing products available. These catalogues indicate covering capacities for various materials which are manufactured in a variety of shapes and sizes.

WOOD SHINGLES

Wood shingles are used as a roof covering on many types of roofs, such as shed, gable, hip, and intersecting. See figure 31, page 59. The first three named are figured alike when estimating the number of shingles, as each has one or more rectangular surfaces. The hip and intersecting roofs require more shingles, due to waste on the hip and valley rafters.

The following rules indicate how to find the area for various types of roofs.

Rule for shed roof: Rafter length times eaves length equals roof area.

Rule for gable roof: Rafter length times ridge length times two equals roof area.

Rule for hip roof: As a hip roof has the same area as a gable roof (on a building having the same dimensions and roof pitch) common rafter length times two equals roof area.

Rule for intersecting roof: This roof is easiest figured on the basis of roof *plan* area. The roof plan area is found by increasing building dimensions by the cornice run. Then multiply the width by the length and deduct any "take-away" areas. See figure 17, page 42. Then multiply the actual plan area of the roof by a constant selected for the required roof pitch. See table XI, page 61.

Rule to find Number of Bundles of Shingles:

a. Roof area divided by the number of square feet of surface covered by one bundle equals number of bundles. Count part of a bundle as a full one. See table XV, page 92.

b. For hip or intersecting roofs figure the same as rule "a" and then add 5% to allow for waste on the hips and valleys.

c.   Hips and ridges are usually shingled by using an extra row laid in such a manner as to make them waterproof. This requires additional shingles. Allow one bundle for every 25 linear feet of hips and ridges.

d. Divide number of bundles by 4 and result is number of four-bundle-squares to order. See note on page 93.

COMPOSITION ROOFING SHINGLES

Composition roofing is sold in rolls 3' wide, 36' long. Each roll contains 108 square feet, but will only cover 100 square feet. The extra 8 square feet, is used for laps to make a water-tight roof. The thickness of the material varies from $\frac{1}{2}$ ply to 3 ply, the latter being the thickest. Composition roofing paper can be bought in various colors and finishes.

At least 12" should be added to the width and length measurements of a flat roof before finding roof area, to allow for the paper turning up at the firewalls. Add more if the plan indicates more height should be turned up as sometimes the roofing goes over the top edge of the firewall.

Rule: Find the roof area and divide by 100. Result equals number of rolls of roofing. Any fractional part of 100 square feet must be counted as a full roll as parts of a roll cannot be purchased.

COMPOSITION SHINGLES

Composition shingles are manufactured in a variety of sizes, colors and finishes. Some are individual shingles which are of uniform width and length, others are made in strips, giving the appearance of individual shingles after they are laid.

All composition shingles are packed in bundles and vary as to the number in each bundle. The following table indicates covering capacities and the number of shingles per square for a variety of sizes.

TABLE XVI

COMPOSITION SHINGLE TABLE*

| SPECIFICATION | KIND | | | |
	Thick Tab	3 Tab 1 kx	Dutch Cap	Hip & Ridge
Size	12″ x 36″	11⅓″ x 36″	12″ x 16″	9″ x 12¾″
App. Wt. per Sq.	210 lb.	168 lb.	164 lb.	253 lb.
Shingles per Sq.	80	86	112	381
Bundle per Sq.	3	2	2	3
Nails per Shingle	6	4	2	2
Exposure	5″	4⅔″	10″	5″
Head lap	2″	2″	3″	2¾″

NOTE: Data courtesy Pabco Products, Inc., Los Angeles, California, as of March 1952.

For hips and valleys roll roofing is used, a 36″ roll being cut into 12″ strips. A strip is first placed in the valley and then the composition roofing shingles are laid. The same process is followed for a hip, except the roll roofing is laid on top of the composition shingles.

Rule: To figure the number of composition shingles required for a roof proceed as follows:

a. Figure the roof area as outlined on page 71.

b. Divide area by 100 to reduce to squares.

c. Multiply number of squares by the number of bundles per square as selected from table XVI. Result equals number of bundles required.

d. Figure linear feet of valleys and hips (see table on page 65). Divide result by 3. Result equals linear feet of 36″ roll roofing required. Divide result by number of linear feet per roll. The number of linear feet in a roll of roofing paper varies. A standard roll is 36′ long and 3′ wide and will cover one square of surface. Result equals number of rolls of roofing to order. Part of a roll must be counted as a full one.

e. If roll roofing is used for the ridge, figure the same as for the hips and valleys. Ridge lengths can usually be scaled on the blueprint.

SLATE ROOFING

Roofing slate is finished in a number of sizes, thicknesses and finishes. The following table indicates the number required per square.

Rule:

a. Figure the net roof area as outlined on page 71.

b. Deduct for openings, such as chimneys and dormers, as follows:
If less than 20 square feet, none.

TABLE XVII
ROOFING SLATE TABLE

| Size of Slate | | Exposure | No. per Square |
Length	Width		
	6″		686
10″	7″	3½″	588
	8″		515
	6″		533
	7″		457
12″	8″	4½″	400
	9″		355
	10″		320
	7″		374
	8″		327
14″	9″	5½″	290
	10″		261
	12″		218
	8″		277
16″	9″	6½″	246
	10″		221
	12″		185
	9″		213
18″	10″	7½″	192
	11″		175
	12″		160
	10″		170
20″	11″	8½″	154
	12″		141
	14″		121
	11″		138
22″	12″	9½″	126

If more than 20 and less than 80, deduct one half of the area of the openings.

If more than 80 square feet, deduct 20 square feet less than the actual area of the openings.

c. Add one square foot for each linear foot of hips and valleys to allow for waste in cutting and fitting.

d. Add from 2% to 15% depending upon the extent to which the roof is cut up.

e. Divide the total obtained by 100 to reduce to squares.

f. Multiply number of squares by number of slate per square. Result equals slate required.

NOTE: There are so many factors to be considered, such as different sizes of slate, different exposures, and the number of dormers and chimneys, that roofing specialists should always be consulted when estimating slate.

CHAPTER V

INTERIOR FINISH

THE INTERIOR FINISH work of a residence is divided, for estimating purposes, into four divisions. Windows, doors, screens, and shutters form the first division. Inside trim is included in the second group. Interior built-in features, such as bookcases and kitchen sink cases are grouped to make the third division. Lastly, comes the finish T&G stock used for floors and occasionally partitions and walls.

WINDOW, SASH, DOOR, AND SHUTTER UNIT

WINDOWS AND SASH

There are several kinds of windows used in a residence. The double hung window has an upper and lower sash which slide vertically. These sash are counterbalanced by weights hung on sash cord or chain, or by a sash balance. A second type is the casement window, technically known as a casement sash. This sash is hinged to swing either in or out. A third kind is the window which does not open and is called a stationary sash. Occasionally a sash will be hinged at the bottom and is called a transom sash.

NOTE: The term "sash" always means a single unit and may open in or out, be hinged at the bottom or be one of the two parts of a double hung window, that is upper or lower sash.

The term "window," when applied to those made of wood is only used for the double hung type. If the window is made of metal then the word "window" means the metal frame *and* the metal sash, all assembled ready for installation.

Size: The width of a window or sash is given first, the length second and the thickness third. If two sash are to be hinged in one frame, they are called a pair. The size of the pair is the same as the size of the frame. To illustrate: An order for a pair of sash for a 4′-0″ x 3′-0″ frame would read: One pair (pr.) casement sash 4′-0″ x 3′-0″ x 1⅜″. The accepted standard thickness of sash is 1⅜″. The joint, where the two sash meet, is known as a rabbetted joint. In taking-off windows, it is advisable to select all like sizes first.

NOTE: In some parts of the United States it is common practice to give only the glass size of a window. From this size the outside measurements of the sash or window must be computed. For a 2 light window with 1⅜″ check rail add 4″ to width and 6″ to length.

To illustrate: A 2 light (lt.) window has a glass size of 24/30. This means the glass in each sash is 24″ wide and 30″ high. 24″ plus 4″ equals 28″ or 2′-4″, which is width. 30″ x 2″ (the double hung window is two sash high) equals 60″. 60″ plus 6″ equals 66″, or 5′-6″ which is length. Therefore, the window frame size is 2′-4″ x 5′-6″.

Kind of lumber: The kind of lumber used for sash will vary according to each locality. Sugar pine or cypress is often used. The specifications will give this information.

Number of Lights: The number of lights of glass in a window will vary according to the way the plan is drawn and the type of architecture used. The elevation sheet will give this information.

TABLE XVIII

THICKNESS AND WEIGHT OF WINDOW GLASS

	Thickness in Inches		Number of Lights per Inch (thickness)		Average Weight in Ounces per Sq. Ft.
	Min.	Max.	Min.	Max.	
Single strength	.080	.100	10.5	12.0	18.5
Double strength	.111	.125	8.0	9.0	24.5
26 oz. glass	.125	.135	7.5	8.0	26.0
29 oz. glass	.135	.148	6.5	7.0	29.0
34 oz. glass	.150	.175	6.0	6.5	34.0
39 oz. glass	.176	.205	5.0	5.5	39.0

Grade of Glass: The United States Government specifies glass as follows: "AA" is first quality, "A" is second quality, and "B" third quality. The plans and specifications should be consulted before any glass is ordered.

Weight of Glass: Glass is also designated by weight. The two weights in common usage are known as single strength, (sometimes called 16 oz.), which averages 18.5 ounces per square foot, and double strength, (sometimes called 21 oz.), which averages 24.5 ounces per square foot. The maximum size recommended for single strength glass is 40" x 50"; for double strength glass, 60" x 80".

Table XVIII indicates the thickness and weight of a number of standard weights of glass.

Plate glass is used in the better class of residential buildings because of its clearness and freedom from waves and defects. This glass is from $\frac{3}{16}$" to $\frac{1}{4}$" thick, (approximately), and the sizes vary from 6″ x 6″ pieces, by even inches, to 144″ x 200″ or 138″ x 208″.

NOTE: Mirrors may be obtained in sizes varying from 4″ x 4″, by even inches, to 84″ x 150″, with bevels varying from 1″ to 2″.

Kind of Glass: There are different kinds of glass that may be used, such as clear and obscure. Obscure glass is obtainable in a number of different patterns. If specifications do not state kind, clear glass is usually understood to be wanted.

Shape of Lights: This information is determined from the elevation sheet, as windows are cut up into many different designs.

Kind of Sticking: The term sticking, when applied to a window refers to the shape of the moulded edge into which glass is fittted. Unless specified, the mill will make the sash to a standard design. If the plans show other than stock design this information must be given on the order.

Catalogue Number: Many large manufacturing plants furnish catalogues to serve as aids in the selection of the correct type and size of their product. If such an aid is available, it is advisable to include on the order the catalogue number of the item.

WINDOW SCREENS

A few years ago it was common practice for the carpenter to make screens on the job. With the development of machinery, however, this job is usually done in a mill or special screen factory.

Only those windows that open require screens. Sometimes screens are not specified, although this practice pertains to public buildings rather than residences.

Considerable information is necessary when ordering screens, as outlined below.

Quantity: Only those screens that are the same in size and kind of wire can be grouped together. To determine the number of screens required, check the specifications to find which windows are to have screens and count those windows on the floor plan. Or, if the symbol "Sc" is printed for each window that requires a screen, as is sometimes done on a plan, count these symbols.

Name of Screen: There are three standard kinds of window screens based on the kind of frame into which they hang.

1. The full double hung window screen has a horizontal bar across it at the meeting point of the two parts of a double-hung window.

2. The sliding screen always moves vertically.

3. If a casement screen is ordered, no bars are put in unless specified. All screens that hinge in are known as "inside screens." The lumber for an inside screen is selected to match the interior finish.

Size: The width of a screen is the same as the width of the sash or window.

The length of a screen is not the same as the sash or window, but longer. This is because of the pitch or slant of the sill. The screen for a casement sash is longer than for a double-hung window on account of different measuring points. Figure 53 illustrates this. When taking-off the screens, add 1″ to the window length. *The exact screen length is determined after the window frame is built.*

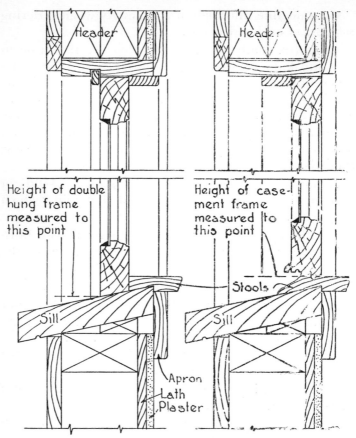

FIG. 53—*Measuring Points for Double-Hung and Casement Sash Window Frames*

The thickness of a screen is determined by the detail of the window frame or the specifications. This thickness will vary, but the standard is recognized as being ¾″ unless otherwise stated.

Kind of Lumber: The kind of lumber will vary, and is based somewhat on local practices. Redwood or sugar pine is often used.

Kind of Wire: This information is given in the specifications. There are four kinds of wire commonly used: black, galvanized, aluminum, and copper. In damp climates copper is used due to its weather resisting qualities.

Kind of Mesh: The wire is ordered by mesh which means the number of holes per linear inch. The wire commonly used is 12, 14, or 16 mesh.

Number of Ligths: The term "light," although usually applied to glass, is also used when ordering screens, and means the openings in the screen frame. As these openings are made to match the window or sash, the same terminology applies.

Window screens usually have one light for a casement sash frame and two lights for a double hung window frame. A bar is placed across the screen parallel to the meeting bar on the double hung windows. Occasionally an architect will specify screens to match the windows.

Shape of Lights: The shape of the lights will usually conform to the window to which the screen belongs.

SHUTTERS

Shutters are becoming a regular part of the exterior design of many homes. In numerous cases they are used for architectural effect only and are not hinged but screwed flat to the wall.

NOTE: Shutters really belong to the exterior finish division of a building, but are usually listed with the door and window mill bid. Hence they are included in this section.

Quantity: The elevation sheets will show which windows require shutters. and indicate their shape. Two shutters are required for each window frame.

Size: If the shutters are to be hinged to shut into the frame, the width will be one-half the width of the window. The length will have to be determined from the window frame detail as the slope of the sill affects the length of the shutter. For estimating purposes add 1″ to the length of the frame. Shutters that are to fit into a frame should not be ordered until the frames are made.

If shutters are used for ornamental purposes only the length should be measured on the elevation sheet as architectural practices vary as to the length of a shutter when used in this way. The width will be one-half the window width.

Kind of Lumber: The specifications will usually state this. White pine is often used.

Shape of the Shutter: The shape of the shutter is determined by checking the elevation sheets. Occasionally architects will draw full size details showing the sizes of the stiles and rails.

DOORS

In making an order for doors there are a number of important facts which must be given.

Quantity: List the number of doors required, grouping only those doors that are alike in every detail.

Name of Door: There are several types of doors commonly used in house construction. These are generally classified as interior, exterior, screen, and cabinet doors.

Size: The width is given first, length second, and thickness third.

Kind of Lumber: The kind of lumber is given in the specifications. They also state whether the door is to be veneered and if the same kind of veneer is to be used on both sides. Often a door is made with different woods on different sides in order to secure certain architectural effects.

Number of Lights or Panels: See page 106 for information on lights. The detail sheet in the set of blueprints will indicate the number of panels required for each door.

Weight of Glass: Plate glass is occasionally used in residential doors, and always used for interior mirror doors. For standard weights of glass see page 107.

Kind of Glass: See page 108.

Grade of Glass: See page 107.

Shape of Lights: See page 108.

Kind of Wire: This only applies to screen doors, and the wire will, of course, match the wire on the window screens. For kind of wire see page 111.

Mesh of Wire: See page 111.

Catalogue Number: See page 108.

INSIDE TRIM UNIT

Inside trim is finished lumber, milled in the form of casings, stool, aprons, door jambs, baseboard, baseshoe, picture moulding, and other parts of interior woodwork.

DOOR JAMBS

A door jamb is the frame into which a door is fitted and hung. It is made of finish lumber S4S, sanded on one side and consists of two side pieces and one top piece, known as the head jamb. Figure 54 represents a door jamb set in place. Each inside door requires one door jamb. A sliding door requires two jambs.

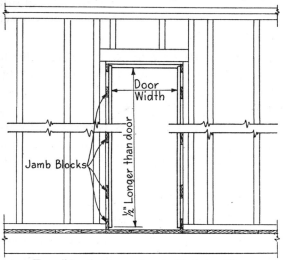

FIG. 54—*A Door Jamb 'Set' in Place*

Two kinds of finish lumber are sometimes required on the inside trim of a house, and the question arises as to which room the door jamb stock should match. The rule is: the finish of the room from which the jamb can be seen when the door is closed, determines the kind of lumber to use. An exeception is made in the case of any small adjacent room, such as a clothes closet. In this situation, the jamb is made of the same kind of lumber as the main room.

Rule: Allow one jamb for each door. Width must be made exactly the same dimension as thickness of the finished wall. Length equals twice door length plus door width plus 6″. Increase to a standard length of lumber.

NOTE: Side jambs are made ½″ longer than the actual length of a door to give clearance under the door. This prevents a door from dragging or rubbing on the floor coverings, such as rugs or linoleum.

DOOR AND WINDOW STOPS

A door stop is a piece of finish stock nailed on the face of a door jamb to serve as a stop against which the door will shut. See figure 55.

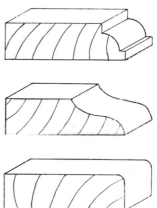

A window stop is used on a double hung window to hold the lower sash in place. It also serves as a stop against which the casement will shut. Sometimes a stop is made a part of the casement jamb, in which case no separate piece is required.

If a different kind of finish lumber is used in some rooms, a door stop always matches the room from which it can be seen when the door is closed.

FIG. 55—*Typical Details of Door or Window Stops*

Rule:

    a. Allow one stop for each inside door. Double acting doors require none. Sliding doors require two stops. Each double hung window requires one stop and each casement sash one stop if the jamb is not rabbetted. Thickness and width measurements are given in the specifications.

b. Add twice the length of a door or window to its width, allow 6″ for fitting, and increase to a standard length of lumber.

NOTE: The term "stop" as used above means the two side pieces and one head piece. These three pieces are combined into one length when ordering. A door or window frame actually has only one stop.

INSIDE CASINGS

Inside casing is finish lumber that covers the space between the rough framed opening and a window frame or door jamb.

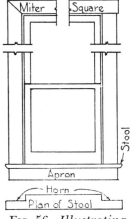

FIG. 56—*Illustrating Window Stool, Apron, Miter and Square Casing Joints*

The kind of lumber for casings is given in the specifications. Often two or more kinds of wood are used in a residence, hard wood being used in the living room and dining room, and less expensive lumber for the remainder of the house.

The shape of the casing is given on a detail sheet of a plan. Any shaped casing can be bought. Only a few patterns are kept in stock and these stock designs do not cost as much as a special design which requires a "sticker setup."

Casing can be bought more economically if short lengths are ordered. The following rules are based on this procedure.

Two types of joints are used, miter or butt. See figure 56 (Butt or square are the same).

Rules for inside doors:

Heads: Allow two pieces for each inside door. Width of door plus twice the width of the side casing stock plus 2″ equals length. Increase to a half-foot or even foot length of lumber.

Sides: Allow four pieces for each inside door:

Butt joint construction: Length equals door height plus 2″. Increase to a half-foot or even foot of lumber.

Miter joint construction: Length equals door height plus width of casing stock plus 2″. Increase to a half-foot or even foot length of stock.

Rules for windows:

Heads: Allow one piece for each window frame. Width of window plus twice the width of the casing stock plus 2″ equals length. Increase to a half-foot length of lumber.

If the frame has a mullion casing, then add the width of each mullion to the result before increasing to the half or even foot length of stock.

Side: Allow two pieces for each window frame.

Butt joint construction: Length equals window height plus 2″. Increase to a half-foot or even foot length of lumber.

Miter joint construction: Length equals window height plus width of casing stock plus 2″. Increase to a half-foot or even foot length of lumber.

Rule for outside doors:

Heads: Allow one piece for each door frame. Width of door plus twice the width of the casing stock plus 2″ equals length. Increase to a half-foot or even foot length of lumber.

Sides: Allow two pieces for each outside door.

Butt joint construction: Length equals door height plus 2″. Increase to a half-foot or even foot length of lumber.

Miter joint construction: Length equals door height plus width of casing stock plus 2″. Increase to a half-foot or even foot length of stock.

Rule for mullion casings: Allow one piece for each mullion in the frame. Length of frame plus 2″ equals length. Increase to a half-foot length of stock.

STOOL

Stool is finish stock fitted and nailed on horizontally at the bottom of a window frame. See figure 56. There are two common types, casement and double hung, as shown in figure 57. The casement type is used for casement or hinged sash, while the other is for double hung windows. The double hung type is also used for stationary windows. An architect will sometimes design a special shaped stool.

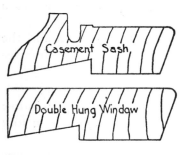

Fig. 57—*Cross Section of Casement Sash Stool and Double Hung Window Stool*

The kind of lumber is given in the specifications and will be the same as the inside finish lumber. There may be more than one kind of lumber required.

Rule: Allow one piece for each window frame. Width of window plus 12″ equals length. Width of all mullion center casings, if any, must also be added to this result. Combine into standard lengths of lumber, but keep each kind of stool separate.

APRON

Apron is the piece of finish stock fitted and nailed underneath a window stool. See figure 56. The kind of lumber is given in the specifications and will be the same as the interior finish. The shape will vary according to the casing detail. The thickness of apron stock is usually ¾″, but the width varies according to the architect's requirements.

Rule: Allow one piece for each window frame. Width of frame plus twice width of casing stock plus 2″ equals length. Combine into standard lengths of lumber.

BASEBOARD, BASEMOULD, AND SHOE

Baseboard is finish stock nailed on a plastered wall at the floor line to form a finish between floor and wall. It is nailed on either before or after plastering depending on the blueprints and specifications. In shape, it varies from the simplest design to a moulded one. Sometimes a basemould is used on the top edge of the baseboard.

Base shoe is a small moulding nailed at the floor line to close the space between the bottom edge of baseboard and the finished floor. Baseboard, basemould, and shoe are usually written as one order.

Rule: The distance around a room (perimeter), less each door or archway opening, increased to next half or whole foot, equals the number of linear feet of baseboard and shoe to order for one room. Repeat for all rooms and closets and then combine results.

NOTE: Baseboard is always fitted against the door casing. There is, therefore, a little extra material allowed for at each opening amounting to twice the width of the casing stock. This is not deducted but included in the total linear feet of baseboard ordered and offsets any split ends or waste due to cutting.

HOOK STRIP

Hook strip is a piece of finish lumber nailed on a closet wall about 5 or $5\frac{1}{2}$ feet from the floor into which coat and hat hooks are screwed.

Rule: Perimeter of the closet, less width of the door and window equals linear feet for one closet. The total of all closets equals amount of hook strip required. Order by linear foot or piece.

PICTURE MOULDING

Picture moulding is nailed on a wall near the ceiling line to hang pictures on, for architectural effects, or to make a break between a plastered ceiling and papered wall.

Rule for linear feet: Room perimeter plus two feet equals linear feet of moulding for one room. Repeat for all rooms that require moulding.

Rule for number of pieces: Allow four pieces to each room. Length equals room measurements. Increase to a standard length of stock.

THRESHOLD

Threshold is finish stock fitted and nailed over the small crack between the inside edge of an exterior door frame sill and the finish floor.

It also serves to fill the space under an outside door, as door jambs are always made ½″ longer than the door to allow it to clear the rugs or other floor covering. This space is not objectionable on an interior door, but must be closed on an exterior door to keep out cold. In localities that experience low temperatures, a metal weather strip, in addition to the threshold, is used to make the joint perfectly tight.

The kind of lumber is given in the specifications. For front doors oak is most often used as it is a durable wood and will match the hardwood floor. For the rear door, vertical grain Douglas fir makes a good threshold.

The size of the threshold is given in the specifications or on the detail sheet of a set of plans. A standard size carried in stock by a mill is ⅝″ x 3½″.

Rule: Allow one piece for each outside door. Door width plus 4″ equals length. Increase to an even foot length of lumber or combine pieces into one standard length.

CABINET UNIT

MILL MADE CABINETS

If the floor plan can be scaled, cabinet sizes are determined by using the architect's scale. Exact sizes are not given until the building is framed ready for plastering, as spaces for cabinets will not always work out to the scale dimensions on the blueprint.

When ordering, there are several important facts which must always be given.

Number of Units: Items identical in size, shape, and kind of wood, should be grouped together.

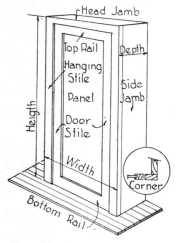

FIG. 58—*Terms Used to Designate Cabinet Sizes and Parts*

Name of the Unit: Several standard cabinets are used in an average house, their names being based either on location or use.

The linen closet is usually in the hall.

Bookcases are found in the living room, den or library.

Dish cupboards and the sink cabinets are in the kitchen.

Medicine cabinets are in the bathroom.

A broom closet is usually constructed on the service porch.

A chest of drawers may be found in the bedroom, dressing closet, bathroom, or powder room.

Size of the Unit: There are three main dimensions required when ordering a cabinet. These are width, height, and depth, as shown in figure 58. It is advisable to see that the mill is provided with a sketch or architect's detail which will indicate the number of drawers and doors required, the location of the shelving, etc.

Kind of Lumber: The kind of lumber used for a cabinet will vary according to its location in the building and the painting specifications. Occasionally cedar is used for drawer bottoms or shelves because of its aromatic qualities.

Special Information: The following special information must be given:

a. Kind of drawer required, whether lip or flush.
   Size of stock for the stiles and rails of the doors.

b. Whether the doors are to have wood or glass panels; and, if glass, the kind of glass, such as clear, frosted, art, 21 oz., 16 oz., and the grade, as AA, A or B. See page 107.

c. If the shelves are to be adjustable.

d. Kind of material to be used for the back of the cabinet. This might be 1″ x 4″ or 1″ x 6″ T&G stock or 3-ply paneling.

JOB MADE CABINETS

Sometimes cabinets are made on the job by the carpenter in which case he orders the proper lengths and sizes of stock necessary for their construction.

PARTS OF A CABINET

Carcase: The main body of the cabinet. This includes two sides, top, bottom, back, shelves and partitions.

Front or Face Frame: The frame into which the doors and drawers are fitted. See figure 87, page 219.

Drawers and Doors: Glass, or wood panel.

Hardware: Pulls, knobs, fasteners, locks, and hinges.

Rule: Make an itemized list showing thickness, width and length of each part of the cabinet. Combine into lengths that will cut without waste.

FLOORING UNIT

HARDWOOD FLOORING

Hardwood flooring is T&G stock made from different hardwoods. There are many grades of material that may be purchased. The factory grade is made from short pieces of discolored lumber which may have small worm holes, while the best grade is of an even color and has a beautiful grain.

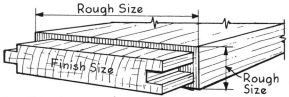

Fig. 59—*Showing Necessity for Mill Allowances When Figuring T & G Stock*

Lumber association rules permit a certain percentage of an order to be short lengths. The poorer quality of material will have more short lengths.

Hardwood flooring may be bought in various widths and thicknesses. As the proportion of stock milled away varies with the original size of different widths of stock, as shown in figure 59, the percentage or fractional increase varies. The table below gives the percentage increase for some standard widths of flooring.

Rule:

a. Find room area which is width of room multiplied by length of room. Use inside measurements as scaled on the blueprints, increasing fractional room measurements to next quarter foot before computing.

b. Fireplace areas should be deducted.

c. Then add to the room area the correct percentage increase as indicated.

TABLE XIX

PER CENT INCREASE FOR STANDARD SIZES OF HARDWOOD FLOORING

Rough Size of Stock	Thickness and Face Width	Percent Increase
1″ x 2″	$\frac{3}{8}$″ x 1$\frac{1}{2}$″	36%
1″ x 2$\frac{1}{2}$″	$\frac{3}{8}$″ x 2″	28%
1″ x 2″	$\frac{1}{2}$″ x 1$\frac{1}{2}$″	36%
1″ x 2$\frac{1}{2}$″	$\frac{1}{2}$″ x 2″	28%
1″ x 2$\frac{1}{4}$″	$\frac{13}{16}$″ x 1$\frac{1}{2}$″	52$\frac{1}{2}$%
1″ x 3″	$\frac{13}{16}$″ x 2$\frac{1}{4}$″	36%

d. Repeat for all rooms.

e. Then add two square feet for each door opening. Result equals square feet of flooring.

PINE FLOORING

The best grade of pine flooring is made from vertical grained lumber as it will not sliver from the wear of walking on it. The sketch in figure 59, shows the end view of a piece of this kind of stock. If the flooring wears down the board still has as smooth a surface as it had originally.

Rules:

a. Floor area plus $\frac{1}{4}$ equals square feet of 4″ stock. Then add 5% for end waste.

b. Floor area plus $\frac{1}{6}$ equals square feet of 6″ stock. Then add 5% for end waste.

c. Short-cut method: Room width measurement (expressed in feet) divided by 3 and multiplied by 11 equals number of 4″ pieces. Room width measurement divided by 3 and multiplied by 7 equals number of 6″ pieces. For 4″ flooring add one extra board for every 12 linear feet of surface. Length of flooring is same as room dimension increased to an even foot length.

T&G CEILING FOR WALLS AND CEILINGS

Sometimes walls, partitions, and ceilings are covered with T&G ceiling in order to make a finished surface.

Square Foot Rule:

a. Find area of wall or partition by multiplying the height by the length.

b. Deduct openings of 10 square feet or more. See table XXXII, page 166.

c. Add $\frac{1}{6}$ to the remaining area. Result is square feet of 6″ T&G stock. If 4″ stock is used, add $\frac{1}{4}$ instead of $\frac{1}{6}$.

Piece Rule: Use short cut rule above for pine floors for figuring T&G ceiling by the piece. Length of ceiling is same as height of wall or room dimensions increased to an even foot length.

CHAPTER VI

HARDWARE

A BUILDING CONTRACTOR'S responsibilities include ordering all fasteners such as nails and bolts required to hold
different parts of a building together and the numerous
items required for interior finish work, such as locks
and hinges.

Builders' hardware is divided into two groups, rough
and finish. Rough hardware includes such items as
common nails, finish nails and bolts. Finish hardware
includes hinges, butts, and locks for doors and windows,
hinges and fasteners for cabinet doors and pulls for
drawers.

ROUGH HARDWARE UNIT

NAILS

Common nails are used for framing work and finish
nails for interior finish. The economical way to buy
nails is by the keg. Nails left from one job are always
usable on the next one.

Rule: Allow 1 keg of 8d box, 1 keg 8d common, ½
keg 16d common. 1 keg of 16d box, and 15 pounds
20d box for 1000 square feet of floor area.

An approximation only can be given for finish
nails. 20 lbs., of 8d finish, 15 lbs. of 6d finish, 1 lb.
of 4d finish, and one package (1 lb.) each of 1″ and
¾″ brads will be required for an average job.

For rules to find quantity of nails required for

different parts of a building see table XXXV, page 175.

NOTE: Many persons are puzzled as to the meaning of the term 8d, 10d, etc. The letter "d" is an abbreviation for the English term "penny." One explanation is that "six penny" means 6 lbs. to each 1,000 nails of this size; 8d meaning 8lbs. to each 1,000 nails of that size, etc.

The number of a nail denotes its length, the larger the number the longer the nail. Table XXXIV, page 174, indicates lengths of various sizes of nails.

BOLTS

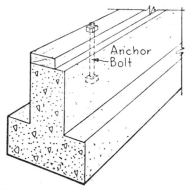

FIG. 60—*Anchor Bolts Used to Hold Down Foundation Sill*

To securely fasten mudsill to a concrete foundation, bolts from 6″ to 8″ in length and ½″ diameter are incased in the concrete before it sets or hardens. See figure 60.

The spacing of the bolts varies according to building ordinances and requirements of an architect. The usual practice is to place them 6′ to 8′ on centers (o.c.).

Rule: Allow one bolt for each 6′ of mudsill; then add one for each corner or angle.

FINISH HARDWARE UNIT

The carpenter-estimator must have a broad knowledge of finish hardware if he is to take-off a bill of hardware correctly. Many kinds of locks can be purchased; hinges and butts come in various shapes and sizes, cabinet doors fasteners are available in many forms; and all can be secured in different finishes.

BASIC INFORMATION

The following basic information applies to all finish hardware items.

Quantity Desired: This is determined by counting the units which require hardware and estimating the number of pieces of hardware needed.

Catalogue Number: To simplify the listing of hardware items a hardware catalogue should be secured. Each item is numbered and sometimes the number is preceded by one or more letters, usually the code for a certain kind of finish. For ordinary types of hardware a catalogue number is not needed. When a special type is required the number is important and should be used.

Manufacturers' Name: For a majority of hardware items no special make is necessary unless specified by the architect. However, there are numerous standard makes of hardware. When ordering a particular piece the manufacturers' name should be included.

Finish of the Hardware: The term "finish" means the decorative appearance of hardware. There are a number of standard finishes such as old copper, black, sand-brass, dull brass, nickel, and sand copper. Hardware for a residence is ordered the same finish throughout excepting the bathroom and kitchen in which nickel hardware is generally used.

Kind of Material: Hardware material is divided into two kinds: steel-plated and solid brass or bronze. Solid brass or bronze is best but more expensive. This quality of hardware is most ofent used on public buildings or costly residences.

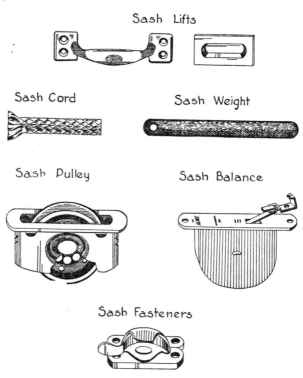

FIG. 61—*Double-Hung Window Hardware*

Size of the Item: The size of a hardware item is stated in the following order: length first, width second, and thickness third.

Name of the Item: To list a hardware bill correctly the name recognized in the building industry should always be given.

DOUBLE HUNG WINDOW HARDWARE

Pulleys: Each window requires four pulleys unless sash balances are used. Several standard types are available.

Sash Cords: Each window requires four cords. The length of each cord is estimated to be the same as the window length. Sash cord is ordered by the hank which contains 100 linear feet. The combined results of the total linear feet of cord required for all the windows is changed to full hanks.

Weight: Four weights are required for each double-hung window, one pair of weights balancing the sash to which they are fastened. Sash weight tables are sufficiently accurate for an estimator. See table XXXIII, page 173.

NOTE: The weight of sash varies depending on the kind of wood and the thickness of glass. It is best to weigh each sash to get accurate results, dividing the weight of each by two. This will give the size weight required. Sash weights should not be ordered until the sash are actually weighed.

Sash Balances: When a narrow trim is used for double hung windows there is no room for sash weights and a sash balance must be used. Balances are made to fit different window sizes. When ordering them the dimensions of the window must be given. One balance is needed for each sash (that is upper and lower) of a double hung window. Large windows require two balances to each sash, or four to a frame.

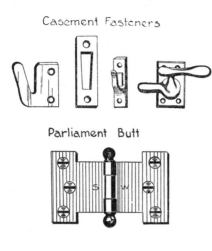

Casement Fasteners

Parliament Butt

Lifts: A sash lift is hardware fastened at the bottom of a window to raise it. There are several types available. One lift for each window is usually sufficient, wide windows require two each.

Locks or Fasteners: The ordinary window requires one sash lock.

CASEMENT SASH HARDWARE

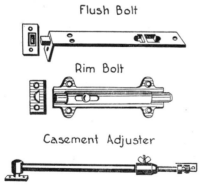

Flush Bolt

Rim Bolt

Casement Adjuster

Fig. 62—*Casement Sash Hardware*

Butts: A casement sash usually requires a special type of hinge known as a parliament butt. It is a wide hinge, designed to permit sash that swing in to be opened to 180 degree angle after the window shades are on. The average sash requires one pair of butts which can be procured in various sizes, the most commonly used being 5″ parliament. These butts are loose pin so the sash may be taken off.

NOTE: "Butt" is the trade term used for a hinge that is screwed onto the *edge* of a door or casement sash. A seat or "dap" is cut to receive one leaf of the butt so that the face of the metal will be flush with the edge. The term "hinge" is applied to hardware screwed onto the *face* of the door or casement sash stile. Because the hinge leaf is exposed it is made ornamental in shape. Round headed screws are often used to give a finished effect.

If the sash opens out, a 3″ x 3″ sheradized tight pin butt is generally used. Sheradized means the hinges have a rust-proof finish.

Fasteners: These are two types of fasteners: one in which the strike is fastened to the jamb, known as "jamb strike"; the other used when there are a pair of sash in the same opening, and known as "surface strike." For an average length casement sash one fastener is sufficient. On long sash two are required.

Bolts: A bolt is always required at the top and bottom end of one unit of a pair of sash. There are two types, the flush bolt and the surface bolt. Order two bolts for each pair of sash.

Adjusters or Casement Operators: If the window opens out, an adjuster is required to keep the sash open and prevent it swinging. Some operate with a handle through the apron, some with a thumb screw adjustment. Order one adjuster for a single sash and two for each pair of casements.

NOTE: On jobs that require rigid economy a large wire hook will be quite satisfactory. The inside window screen must be opened to use the hook.

Hook and Eye

Screen Hanger

Hook Sash Lift

FIG. 63— *Window Screen Hardware*

WINDOW SCREEN HARDWARE

The finish hardware required to hang a window screen is selected on the basis of whether the screen opens out, opens in and is hinged at the side, as a casement sash, or slides vertically.

Screen Opening Out

Hangers: These are fasteners at the top of a window screen which permit the screen to open and also be lifted off. One pair of hangers is required for each screen.

Hook and Eye: A hook and eye is required at the bottom of a screen to secure it in position. Wide screens require two hooks and eyes.

Screen Opening In

Butts and Fasteners: If a casement sash opens out, the screen will be on the inside and require a loose pin butt. The fastener will be the same as for a casement sash. See figure 62.

Sliding Screen

Lifts, Hooks, and Eyes: One lift is required for each sliding screen. One hook and eye will be needed to lock the screen.

FRONT DOOR HARDWARE

Locks: Front door locks may be purchased in a variety of types and designs. Many specifications call for cylin-

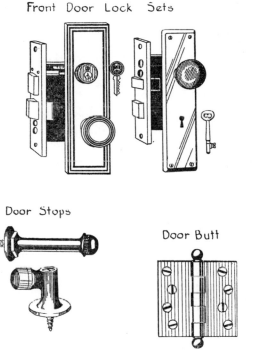

Fig. 64—*Front Door Hardware*

der locks. A lock often used has a night latch instead of a cylinder.

Particular care must be exercised when ordering door locks. A complete lock including escutcheon plates, strike plates, knobs and lock is known as a lock set. Unless the word "set" is used when ordering, the hardware dealer will send only the lock.

Butts: Butts for a front door are usually larger in size than for an inside door. A size commonly used is 4″ x 4″ and one pair is required. A third butt is often put on at the center to prevent the door from becoming warped or twisted, as the outside face of an exterior door is exposed to the weather. Three butts are known as 1½ pairs of butts.

Door Stops or Bumpers: A door stop is a small device which prevents a door handle from striking the wall. There are two types: one is screwed into the baseboard, the other into the floor. The former is preferable. Allow one bumper per door.

SCREEN DOOR HARDWARE

Hinges: There are two types of screen door spring hinges. One is a non-adjustable surface hinge, the other an adjustable hinge. The latter is the best and is made either a surface or edge hinge. A third hinge, placed at the center of a door, prevents the door from becoming warped.

Estimate 1½ pairs screen door hinges for each screen door. A pair of screen doors requires three pairs of hinges.

Fasteners: Usually one hook and eye is used on the inside of a screen door and a 3″ wire handle, or pull, is used on the outside. A small mortise lock is the best

Adjustable Hinge

Screen Door Set

Mortise Catch

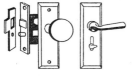

FIG. 65—*Screen Door Hardware*

type of fastener to buy, one being required for each door.

NOTE: A screen door spring hinge set is obtainable and includes a surface hinge, wire hook and handle.

INSIDE DOOR HARDWARE

Butts: The standard size butt used on inside doors is $3\frac{1}{2}''$ x $3\frac{1}{2}''$ loose pin (L.P.), one pair being required for each door.

Locks: A complete lock for an inside door is known as an inside mortise lock set. A French door requires a French door lock, as the stile for this door is narrower than a regular door stile and a standard size lock would be too large. A rabbetted lock must be ordered when a pair of French doors is used if the doors meet. These locks are purchased either right or left hand depending on the way the door swings. This point should be checked carefully before ordering the lock.

The shape of escutcheon plates varies and must be selected before a lock can be ordered.

Locks may have a different finish on each escutcheon. This is to make the door hardware match in each room. For example a hall might have brass finish and the kitchen nickel finish. The lock would require one brass escutcheon and one nickel. The butt finish is determined by the hardware finish of the room into which the door opens.

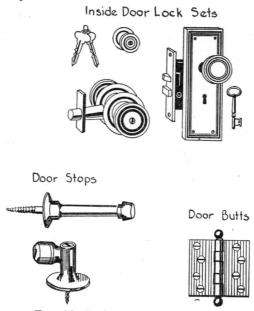

Inside Door Lock Sets

Door Stops

Door Butts

FIG. 66—*Inside Door Hardware*

Door Stops and Bumpers: Allow one stop or bumper for each interior single acting door.

DOUBLE-ACTING DOOR HARDWARE

Hinges: A double-acting door requires a double acting hinge to permit it to open both ways. Some hinges are set into the floor, some screwed to the floor, and others are used on the edge of the door. The more commonly used hinge is the floor type. Each double-acting door requires one hinge.

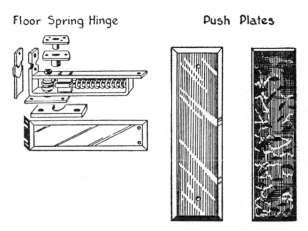

Floor Spring Hinge   Push Plates

FIG. 67—*Double-Acting Door Hardware*

Push Plates: A push plate is the hardware unit screwed to the stile on both sides of a double-acting door to keep the door free from finger prints. There are two types, one of steel or bronze and the other glass. One pair is required for each double-acting door.

CABINET DOOR HARDWARE

Butts or Hinges: A cabinet door requires one pair of butts or hinges. A loose pin butt or an ornamental hinge is used. 1½ pairs of butts or hinges are required on long doors.

Cupboard Turns and Catches

Ornamental Hinges

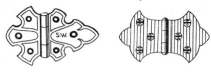

Door Knobs   Butt

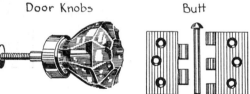

Friction and Elbow Catches

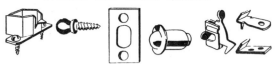

FIG. 68—*Cabinet Door Hardware*

Cupboard Turns or Fasteners: There are many types of fasteners for a cabinet door. One is required for each door.

Elbow or Friction Catches: When two cabinet doors are fitted and hinged into the same opening (known as a pair of doors) one of them, usually the left, must be locked to the cabinet from the inside. For this purpose an elbow or friction catch is used. Allow one catch for each pair of doors.

Glass Door Knobs: When certain types of catches are used one glass knob will be required for each door.

DRAWER HARDWARE

Knobs or Pulls: An ordinary drawer always requires one pull or knob. Wide drawers require two each.

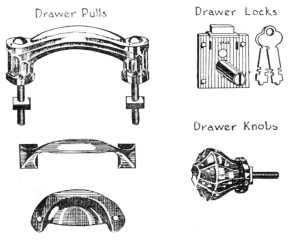

Drawer Pulls   Drawer Locks

Drawer Knobs

Fig. 69—*Drawer Hardware*

Locks: Allow one lock per drawer when locks are specified.

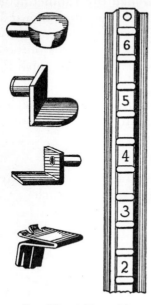

ADJUSTABLE SHELF HARDWARE

Shelf Rests: Adjustable shelves require special hardware to support them. A metal shelf rest is often used. Four are required for each shelf.

Shelf Fixtures: Metal adjustable shelf fixtures are sometimes used and placed vertically in each corner of a case, four being required for one cabinet. The length is the same as (or a little less than) the distance between the top and bottom jambs. Adjustable supports fit into the fixture. Allow four supports for each shelf.

FIG. 70—*Adjustable Shelf Hardware*

COAT AND HAT HOOKS

Closets used for hanging clothes require coat and hat

FIG. 71—*Clothes Closet Hardware*

hooks. There are several types available, two common types being illustrated.

The hooks are screwed to the hook strip and spaced from 6″ to 9″ on centers.

Rule: Estimate the linear feet of hook strip in a closet and divide this number by the spacing of the hooks. Results equals the number of hooks required for one closet. Repeat for all closets. It is not necessary to have an exact count as hooks are usually ordered on the dozen basis.

NOTE: Frequently, the journeyman carpenter is required to purchase building hardware, especially on repair jobs. This can be done in an intelligent manner because he has a good background of hardware information.

The carpenter apprentice will find it very much worthwhile to visit a good hardware store and inspect the various items of builders' hardware in order to become familiar with the many different kinds of materials, finishes, shapes and sizes of hardware units.

CHAPTER VII

BUILDING INFORMATION
AND TABLES

THE BUSINESS OF "TAKING-OFF" a bill of material requires an estimator to have a fund of information readily at hand. The following pages include a number of estimating tables for quick reference.

BUILDING GUIDE

The table below includes numerous items necessary to construct an average dwelling. It covers a building problem from the time the lot is purchased until the owner moves in.

Three persons are responsible for supervision, required when constructing a house, namely; the owner, the architect, and the contractor. An owner has the responsibility of financing, selecting the site, selecting an architect, sometimes selecting a contractor, or conferring with his architect when bids are opened. He has other minor responsibilities such as fire insurance coverage and inspecting the work as the job progresses.

An architect's work consists of designing and drawing plans and specifications according to an owner's wishes. He may have the supervision of the construction work which is very desirable and valuable.

A contractor's responsibilities are those of ordering materials, figuring the necessary labor, letting contracts to sub-contractors, planning and supervising the construction work, and hiring all construction labor.

Trade practice varies considerably as to procedures a contractor will follow in constructing a dwelling. In some cases he may assume all responsibilities as given below, drawing plans and specifications, taking care of financing and supervising actual construction work. In other cases he will limit his work to constructional problems only.

A list of contracts, sub-contracts, materials and miscellaneous items required in the erection of a five room house is given in the table below.

TABLE XX

BUILDING GUIDE

I. Owner's Responsibilities

Buying Lot
  Taxes
  Plot Survey
  Escrow
  Commissions
	Sewer
	  Storm drain
		Fire Insurance

		Curtains

	Loan Costs
	  Appraisal fee
	  Commission
		Draperies
		  Rods

Assessments
  Street improvements
  Street lights
	Guarantee of title	Moving Costs

	Water Connection	

II. Architect's Responsibilities

Drawing Plans and Specifications	Drawing up Contracts	Superintendence

III. Contractor's Responsibilities

A. *Materials*

Lumber
  Framing
  Finish

Hardware
  Rough
  Finish

Millwork
  Outside finish
  Inside finish
  Sash and doors

B. *Sub-Contractors*

Grading

Excavating
  Basement
  Footings

Concrete Work
  Foundation footings
    and walls
  Piers
  Basement and re-
    taining walls
  Flat work
    Fireplace footings
    Driveway
    Garage floors
    Porch floors
    Basement floor
    Walks
  Steps, front and rear
  Street entrance
    driveway

Plumbing
  Roughing in
    Cesspool
  Sewer connections
  Gas lines

Hose bibs
Fixtures
Pipe railings

Refrigeration

Electrical
  Wiring
  Switches
  Bells
  Buzzers
  Fixtures
  Meter Box

Sheet Metal
  Gutters
  Downspouts
  Flashings
  Conductor heads
  Valley tin
  Hood vents
  Decks

Heating
  Furnace
  Register boxes
  Heater vents

Brickwork
  Walls
  Fireplace
    Brick
    Cleanout
    Ash dump
    Terra cotta lining

Roofing
  Built-up roof
  Tile
  Shingle

Plastering
  Exterior
    Lath

Building paper
Plaster
Interior
  Lath
  Metal corner
  Plaster

Screens
  Hung in place

Tile Work
  Sink
  Bathroom floor
  Bathroom base
  Fireplace hearth
    and box

Painting
  Exterior
  Interior
  Tinting

Papering
  Walls
  Ceilings
  Panels

Hardwood Floors
  Flooring
  Laying
  Finishing

Sprinkling System

Landscaping

Wrought Iron

Steel Sash

C. *Labor*

Carpentry
  Lay-out
  Forms

III. Contractor's Responsibilities (*Continued*)

Frames	Social Security	Overhead garage
Finish	insurance	doors
Case work	Sales tax	
Shingling		Interior
	Special Materials	Linoleum
Clearing Lot	Insulation	Mirrors
	Weather stripping	Special glass
Surveying	Waterproofing	Mantels
	Building and insu-	Wall beds
Hauling	lation paper	Venetian blinds
		Window shades
Window Cleaning	Special Parts	
		Built-in accessories
D. *Miscellaneous*	Exterior	Mail box
	Foundation vents	Shoe racks
Permits, insurance	Attic vents	Medicine cabinets
and tax	Awnings	Door grills
Building permits	Fence	Milk bottle holder
and fees	Staff work	Iron receptacle
Liability insurance	Water meter	

LUMBER CHECKING LIST

Lumber needed for an average dwelling is listed below. It is organized on the construction basis. Each item appears on the list in about the same order as used on the job.

Sometimes a builder will construct window frames, a stairway, or built-in cases "on the job." When this is done, the estimator makes out an itemized mill bill for these parts of a house.

The table is divided into two parts, namely, *Framing and Exterior Finish*. Lumber for the interior *finish* is listed separately in table XXII, page 150. The materials are listed on the same basis as the estimating divisions and units given on page 2.

TABLE XXI

LUMBER CHECKING LIST

I. FRAMING

1. *Form Unit*
   Form Boards
   Braces
   Stakes
   Whalers
   Bolts

2. *Underpinning Unit*
   Mudsill
   Pier Blocks
   Posts
   Cribbing Plates
   Cribbing Studs
   Girders
   Braces
   Wedges (shingles)

3. *Floor Unit*
   Joists
   Headers
   Bridging
   Furring (lath)
   Braces
   Sub Floor
   Pine Flooring
   Building Paper

4. *Wall and Partition Unit*
   Plates
   Studs
   Backing
   Firestops
   Braces
   Cove Brackets
   Plaster Grounds
   Sheathing

5. *Ceiling Unit*
   Joists
   Backing
   Stiffeners
   Bridging

6. *Roof Unit*
   Rafters:
      Common
      Hip
      Valley
      Jack
   Braces and Purlines
   Collar Ties
   Frieze or Filler
   Gable Studs
   Sheathing

7. *Stair Unit*
   Horses
   Rough Treads

LUMBER CHECKING LIST *(Continued)*

II. EXTERIOR FINISH

1. *Window or door-frame parts*:
   - Casement Jamb
   - Door Jamb
   - Pulley Stile
   - Blind Stop
   - Parting Bead
   - Sill
   - Side Casing
   - Head Casing
   - Mullions
   - Apron
   - Brick Mould
   - Plaster Mould
   - Window Capping
   - Sash Pulleys
   - Sash Balances

2. *Wall Unit*
   - Belt Course
   - Water Table
   - Siding
   - Building Paper
   - Corner Boards
   - Frieze
   - Shingles

3. *Cornice Unit*
   - Lookouts
   - Brackets
   - Verge Rafters
   - T & G Stock
   - Frieze
   - Plancher
   - Fascia
   - Mouldings

4. *Roof Unit*
   - Wood Shingles
   - Composition Roofing
   - Composition Shingle

5. *Porch Unit*
   - Beams:
     - Sides
     - Soffit
   - Ceiling:
     - T & G Stock
     - Mouldings
   - Solid Posts
   - Built Up Posts
     - Sides
     - Base
     - Cap
     - Moulding
   - Railing:
     - Buttress Cap
     - Lower Rail
     - Balusters
     - Fillet

6. *Bay Windows*
   - Base
   - Casings
   - Frieze
   - Mouldings

MILLWORK CHECKING LIST

This table shows an itemized list of millwork necessary to construct an average dwelling.

TABLE XXII

MILLWORK CHECKING LIST

I. Exterior Finish

1. *Frame Unit*
   Window or door frames complete
   Louvres
   Vents

2. *Shutters (ordered with interior finish)*

II. Interior Finish

1. *Sash, Door, Screen, and Shutter Unit*
   Window and Sash:
   Double Hung Windows
   Casement Sash
   Stationary Sash
   Transom Sash

   Doors:
   Front
   Interior
   Screen

   Window Screens:
   Exterior
   Interior

   Shutters

2. *Trim Unit*
   Window Trim:
   Casing
   Stool
   Apron
   Stops
   Mullions

   Door Trim:
   Jamb
   Casing
   Threshold

   Wall Trim:
   Base
   Base Shoe
   Picture Moulding

II. Interior Finish (*Continued*)

Cornice Moulding
Hook Strip
Clothes Rod
Shelving
Cedar Lining
Drapery Boxes

3. *Cabinet Unit*

  Cabinets Complete:
   Medicine
   Broom
   Sink
   Linen
   Book
   Ironing Board

  Cabinet Parts:
   Carcase
    Top
    Bottom
    Sides
    Shelves
    Divisions
    Back:
     3 ply panel
     T & G ceiling
    Drawer Guides

Face Frame:
   Stiles
   Rails
   Muntins
Drawers:
   Front
   Sides
   Back
   Bottom
Bread Boards

4. *Floor Unit*
   Pine Flooring
   Hardwood Flooring
   3 ply under linoleum

5. *Stair Unit*
   Stairway Parts:
    Stringers
    Treads
    Risers
    Newel Posts
    Balusters
    Fillet
    Hand Rail
    Well Hole Apron
    Mouldings

HARDWARE CHECKING LIST

The following list of hardware includes the major items of rough and finish hardware required for an average dwelling.

TABLE XXIII
HARDWARE CHECKING LIST
I. Rough Hardware

1. *Nails*
   20d Common
   16d Common
   8d Common
   8d Box
   6d Box
   Shingle
   8d Finish
   6d Finish
   4d Finish
   Brads

2. *Bolts*

3. *Garage Doors*
   Hangers and Track
   Hasps
   Hinges
   Bolts

II. Finish Hardware

1. *Doors*
   Butts
   Locks
   Bumpers
   Bolts

2. *Windows*
   Locks
   Lifts
   Pulleys
   Cords
   Weights
   Balances

3. *Sash*
   Butts
   Fasteners
   Bolts
   Adjusters
   Transom Chains

4. *Screens*
   Hangers
   Hooks and Eyes
   Hinges
   Fasteners
   Lifts

5. *Cabinets*
   Doors
   Hinges
   Turns
   Catches
   Drawers
   Pulls
   Lock

6. *Closets*
   Coat and Hat Hooks

7. *Miscellaneous*
   House Numbers
   Cold Glue

8. *Metal Accessories*
   Mail Box
   Shoe Racks
   Door Grilles
   Medicine Cabinet
   Milk Bottle Holder
   Iron Receptacle

BUILDING MATERIALS ORDERING INFORMATION

The following table outlines information which an estimator should know concerning a number of commonly used building materials.

TABLE XXIV

MATERIALS ORDERING INFORMATION
I. MASONRY MATERIALS

1. *Cement*
     Number of sacks
     Kind:
       Portland
       Waterproof
       White
2. *Sand*
     Number of tons or yards
     Kind:
       Plastering
       Concrete
3. *Rock*
     Number of tons or yards
     Size or grade
4. *Brick*
     Number of M
     Kind:
       Common
       Pressed
       Clinker, etc.
     Color
     Cut:
       Wire cut
       Sand-rolled, etc.
5. *Metal Lath*
     Number of yards
     Kind
     Finish:
       Black

6. *Plaster*
     Number of sacks
     Kind of material:
       Hardwall:
         fibered
         unfibered
         sanded
       Stucco
       Finishing
     Manufacturer's Name
     Setting time:
       10 minutes
       20 minutes
       30 minutes
7. *Floor and Wall Tile*
     Number of square feet
         or
     Number of linear feet
         or
     Number of pieces
     Kind:
       American or foreign
       Color
       Shape
       Size
     Weight:
       3.4 lbs.,
       4.0 lbs., etc.
       Galvanized

II. Hardware and Glass
Hardware

1. *Bolts*
    Pcs., doz. or box
    Diameter
    Length
    Kind:
        Carriage
        Machine
        Stove

2. *Finish Hardware*
    No. of pcs., or doz.
    Kind of material:
        Plated or solid
    Kind of finish:
        Brass
        Black
        Copper, etc.

3. *Nails*
    Keg or lb.
    Penny
    Kind:
        Finish
        Box
        Common
        Cement, etc.

4. *Screws*
    Doz. or box
    Number
        (gauge or diameter)
    Length
    Kind of head:
        Round
        Flat
    Material:
        Steel
        Brass

5. *Screen Wire Cloth*
    Linear ft. or roll
    Width
    Mesh:
        12, 14, 16
    Kind:
        Galvanized
        Black
        Copper
        Aluminum

Glass

1. *Dimensions*
    Piece
    Width
    Length
    Thickness:
        16 oz.
        21 oz.

2. *Kind*
    Plate
    Clear
    Wire
    Moss
    Art
    Leaded
    Florentine, etc

3. *Grade*
    A-A, A, etc.

III. Lumber and Millwork

Lumber

---

1. *Rough or Finish*
   No. pcs., linear feet,
     board feet or square
   feet
   Thickness
   Width
   Length
   Grade:
     No. 1 or
     No. 3, etc.
   Kind:
     Douglas fir,
     Sugar pine, etc.
   Milling:
     S4S, S1S, etc.

2. *Shingles*
   No. of bundles or
     'squares'
   Kind of lumber
   Thickness of butt as
     5/2, 6/2, etc.

3. *Lath*
   Kind (wood or plaster)
   Thickness
   Width
   Length
   Grade

Millwork

---

1. *Doors*
   Number
   Width
   Length
   Thickness
   Kind of lumber
   Kind of door:
     Five panel
     Sash, colonial, etc.
   Number of lights of glass
     Kind of glass
       (see glass)

2. *Windows*
   Number
   Width
   Length
   Thickness
   Kind:
     Casement
     Double hung
     Stationary
   Number of lights
   Kind of lumber)
     (see lumber)
   Kind of glass
     (see glass)

3. *Mouldings*
   Pieces or linear feet
   Size (based on cata-
     logue number)
   Kind of lumber

IV. Miscellaneous

1. *Paint*
   Quart or gallon
   Inside or outside
   Color

2. *Oil*
   Quart or gallon
   Boiled or raw

3. *Varnish*
   Quart or gallon
   Inside or outside
   Dull or gloss

4. *Paint Minerals*
   Number of pounds
   Color

5. *Pipe*
   Pieces or linear feet
   Diameter, inside
   Kind:
   Galvanized or black

6. *Roofing Paper*
   Number of rolls
   Weight
   Ply: 2, 3, etc.
   Color
   Finish:
   Sand

7. *Roofing Shingles*
   Size
   Color
   Weight

8. *Roofing Slate*
   Size
   Thickness
   Finsh

9. *Roofing Tile*
   Size
   Shape
   Color
   Design (name)

10. *Sheet Metal*
    Number of Sheets
    Width
    Length
    Gauge
    (thickness)
    16, 20, 22, 24, etc.

11. *Reinforcing Steel*
    Shape (square or round)
    Size
    Length
    Straight or deformed

12. *Canvas (Deck)*
    Weight
    Grade
    Color
    Size

13. *Wire*
    Diameter
    Lbs.
    Kind:
    Galvanized
    Black
    Copper

14. *Angle Iron*
    Thickness
    Width of webs
    Length

BUILDING MATERIAL PURCHASING UNITS

This table indicates the purchasing unit of the most commonly used building materials.

TABLE XXV

BUILDING MATERIAL PURCHASING UNITS

ROOFING MATERIALS:	108 sq. ft. equals 1 roll (36″ wide). 1 roll covers one square.
BUILDING PAPER:	500 sq. ft. equals 1 roll (36″ wide)
FELT PAPER:	(a) 500 sq. ft. equals 1 roll (36″ wide) of 8, 10 and 12 lb. felt.
	(b) 324 sq. ft. equals 1 roll (36″ wide) of 15 lb. felt.
WOVEN WIRE NETTING:	50 sq. yds. equals 1 roll (36″ wide).
WOOD SHINGLES:	4 bundles equals 1000 shingles or one roof-square. 3 bundles equals one side-wall sq.
LATH:	1 bundle equals 100 lath.
CEMENT:	1 sack equals 94 lbs.
SAND:	1 cu. yd. equals 2.78 to 1.3 tons.
ROCK:	1 cu. yd. equals 1.3 tons (approx.).
NAILS:	1 keg equals 100 lbs.
SCREWS:	1 box equals 144 screws (except in very large sizes).
SASH CORD:	1 hank equals 100 lin. ft. (2 hanks are connected).

BOARD FOOT CONSTANT TABLE

The following table is a short-cut method that may be used to find the number of board feet in a piece of lumber. Column I is a list of different sizes of lumber. Column II lists the constants for the corresponding sizes.

TABLE XXVI
BOARD FOOT CONSTANT TABLE

I	II	III
Sizes of Lumber	Fractional Constants	Decimal Constants
1 x 2	1/6	.166
1 x 3	1/4	.25
1 x 4 or 2 x 2	1/3	.33
1 x 5	5/12	.416
1 x 6 or 2 x 3	1/2	.50
1 x 8 or 2 x 4	2/3	.67
1 x 10	5/6	.832
1 x 12 or 2 x 6	1	1.00
2 x 8 or 4 x 4	4/3	1.33
2 x 10	5/3	1.67

To use the table proceed as follows:

1. Select the size of the lumber in Column I.
2. Read the table horizontally and select the constant for that size.
3. Multiply the length of the piece of lumber, or the number of linear feet of lumber, by this constant. Result is the number of board feet. A part of a foot is counted as another whole one.

PERIMETER TABLE

The following table is convenient to use when estimating base, picture moulding, or interior cornice moulding. The left hand vertical column and the top horizontal column indicate room dimensions.

TABLE XXVII
PERIMETER OF ROOMS

	4'	5'	6'	7'	8'	9'	10'	11'	12'	13'	14'	15'	16'	17'	18'	19'	20'
4'	16	18	20	22	24	26	28	30	32	34	36	38	40	42	44	46	48
5'	18	20	22	24	26	28	30	32	34	36	38	40	42	44	46	48	50
6'	20	22	24	26	28	30	32	34	36	38	40	42	44	46	48	50	52
7'	22	24	26	28	30	32	34	36	38	40	42	44	46	48	50	52	54
8'	24	26	28	30	32	34	36	38	40	42	44	46	48	50	52	54	56
9'	26	28	30	32	34	36	38	40	42	44	46	48	50	52	54	56	58
10'	28	30	32	34	36	38	40	42	44	46	48	50	52	54	56	58	60
11'	30	32	34	36	38	40	42	44	46	48	50	52	54	56	58	60	62
12'	32	34	36	38	40	42	44	46	48	50	52	54	56	58	60	62	64
13'	34	36	38	40	42	44	46	48	50	52	54	56	58	60	62	64	66
14'	36	38	40	42	44	46	48	50	52	54	56	58	60	62	64	66	68
15'	38	40	42	44	46	48	50	52	54	56	58	60	62	64	66	68	70
16'	40	42	44	46	48	50	52	54	56	58	60	62	64	66	68	70	72
17'	42	44	46	48	50	52	54	56	58	60	62	64	66	68	70	72	74
18'	44	46	48	50	52	54	56	58	60	62	64	66	68	70	72	74	76
19'	46	48	50	52	54	56	58	60	62	64	66	68	70	72	74	76	78
20'	48	50	52	54	56	58	60	62	64	66	68	70	72	74	76	78	80
21'	50	52	54	56	58	60	62	64	66	68	70	72	74	76	78	80	82
22'	52	54	56	58	60	62	64	66	68	70	72	74	76	78	80	82	84
23'	54	56	58	60	62	64	66	68	70	72	74	76	78	80	82	84	86
24'	56	58	60	62	64	66	68	70	72	74	76	78	80	82	84	86	88
25'	58	60	62	64	66	68	70	72	74	76	78	80	82	84	86	88	90

To use the table proceed as follows: 1. Read the blueprint and find room dimensions. 2. Find these two dimensions on the table, one in the left hand column and the other in the top line. 3. Read the figure at the point found by moving the finger horizontally and vertically from the two numbers selected. This figure is the distance around the room.

CONCRETE FOOTING AND WALL TABLE

The following table will simplify the estimator's work when figuring concrete materials. Each constant indicates the number of cubic feet of form content for one linear foot of footing or wall which has cross section measurements as shown.

TABLE XXVIII

CONCRETE FOOTING AND WALL TABLE

	6"	8"	10"	12"	14"	16"	18"	20"	22"	24"	30"	32"	36"
6"	.25	.33	.42	.5	.58	.66	.75	.83	.92	1.00	1.25	1.33	1.5
8"	.33	.44	.55	.66	.78	.89	1.00	1.11	1.22	1.33	1.66	1.77	2.0
10"	.42	.55	.69	.83	.97	1.11	1.25	1.39	1.53	1.67	2.07	2.22	2.5
12"	.5	.66	.83	1.00	1.17	1.33	1.50	1.66	1.83	2.00	2.50	2.74	3.0
14"	.58	.78	.97	1.17	1.33	1.55	1.75	1.94	2.14	2.33	2.92	3.11	3.5
16"	.66	.89	1.11	1.33	1.55	1.78	2.00	2.22	2.44	2.67	3.33	3.55	4.0
18"	.75	1.00	1.25	1.50	1.75	2.00	2.25	2.50	2.75	3.00	3.75	4.00	4.5
20"	.83	1.11	1.39	1.66	1.94	2.22	2.50	2.78	3.05	3.33	4.17	4.44	5.0
22"	.92	1.22	1.53	1.83	2.14	2.44	2.75	3.05	3.36	3.67	4.58	4.88	5.5
24"	1.00	1.33	1.67	2.00	2.33	2.67	3.00	3.33	3.67	4.00	5.00	5.33	6.0

To use the table proceed as follows: 1. Read the foundation plan and find width and depth of footings and width and height of walls. 2. Select these sizes in the table and read the corresponding constant. 3. Multiply the linear feet of footing or wall by this constant. Result equals the number of cubic feet of form content to use as the basis for estimating concrete materials. See page 22.

CONCRETE PIER TABLE

The table below indicates the approximate cubic footage in each of a number of different sized concrete piers. The constants given are for square and round piers, exclusively.

TABLE XXIX

CONCRETE PIER TABLE

Size of square piers (inches)						Size of round piers (inches)				
Height (inches)	10″	12″	14″	16″	18″	10″	12″	14″	16″	18″
12″	.7	1.0	1.4	1.8	2.2	.5	.8	1.1	1.4	1.8
14″	.8	1.2	1.6	2.1	2.6	.6	.9	1.2	1.6	2.1
16″	.9	1.3	1.8	2.4	3.0	.7	1.0	1.4	1.9	2.4
18″	1.0	1.5	2.0	2.7	3.4	.8	1.2	1.6	2.1	2.6
20″	1.2	1.7	2.3	3.0	3.8	.9	1.3	1.8	2.3	2.9
22″	1.3	1.8	2.5	3.3	4.1	1.0	1.4	2.0	2.6	3.2
24″	1.4	2.0	2.7	3.6	4.5	1.1	1.6	2.1	2.8	3.5

To use the table proceed as follows:

1. Read the foundation plan and find sizes and height of concrete piers.

2. Select this size in the table and read the corresponding constant.

3. Multiply the number of piers by this constant. Result equals the number of cubic feet of pier content to use as a basis for estimating concrete materials. See page 24.

4. If piers are tapered, add top and bottom measurements together and divide by two. Then select this size in the table and read the constant.

NOTE: This is not an exact mathematical procedure but is sufficiently accurate for all practical purposes.

WINDOW FRAME TABLE

The following table indicates the lengths of stock required to make certain parts of a window frame. It includes various standard sizes of windows.

The lengths given are based on using ordinary window or door frame construction, with standard width casings. If special details are given the material should be figured as described on page 81-88.

The special detail should be studied carefully and the types of construction required at each joint noted. Combine all additional material required for the various joints. This is added to the length of stock previously found by adding the width of the frame to twice its length.

Mullion and triplet frames will likewise need to be figured on the basis of the construction required and the width of the mullions, which are never of a standard width.

The table does not include the sill stock as that is always a different shape and size than the jamb stock or pulley stile.

All odd number lengths of stock must be ordered the next even length of stock, unless more than one frame is required. In that case, combine lengths less than 10′.

TABLE XXX
WINDOW FRAME TABLE

Size of Sash	I Window Jamb or Pulley Stile	II Outside Casing	III Plaster Mould Blind Stop Parting Bead
1'-0" x 2'-0"	6'	6'	6'
1'-6" x 2'-0"	7'	7'	7'
2'-0" x 2'-0"	7'	7'	7'
2'-0" x 2'-6"	8'	8'	8'
3'-6" x 2'-6"	10'	10'	10'
1'-6" x 3'-0"	9'	9'	9'
2'-0" x 3'-0"	9'	9'	9'
2'-6" x 3'-0"	10'	10'	10'
3'-0" x 3'-0"	10'	10'	10'
3'-6" x 3'-0"	12'	12'	12'
2'-0" x 3'-6"	10'	10'	10'
3'-0" x 3'-6"	12'	12'	12'
3'-6" x 3'-6"	12'	12'	12'
1'-6" x 4'-0"	12'	12'	12'
2'-0" x 4'-0"	12'	12'	12'
2'-6" x 4'-0"	12'	12'	12'
3'-0" x 4'-0"	12'	12'	12'
3'-6" x 4'-0"	14'	14'	14'
4'-0" x 4'-0"	14'	14'	14'
2'-0" x 4'-6"	12'	12'	12'
2'-6" x 4'-6"	14'	14'	14'
1'-6" x 5'-1"	14'	14'	14'
2'-0" x 5'-1"	14'	14'	14'
2'-6" x 5'-1"	16'	16'	16'
3'-0" x 5'-0"	14'	14'	14'
4'-0" x 5'-0"	14'	14'	14'

To use the table proceed as follows:
1. Read the size of the window for which a frame is to be made.
2. Select this size and read horizontally. Each number indicates length of lumber required.

DOOR FRAME, INSIDE DOOR JAMB
AND DOOR STOP TABLE

There are certain lengths of lumber that can be ordered for a door frame, an inside door jamb, and a door stop which will cut with the least waste. The following table indicates these lengths for different size doors.

TABLE XXXI

DOOR FRAME, INSIDE DOOR JAMB, AND DOOR STOP TABLE

I	II	III
Size of Door	Length of Stocks for Door Jambs or Outside Casings	Door Stop
2'-0" x 6'-6"	16'	16'
2'-4" x 6'-6"	16'	16'
2'-6" x 6'-6"	16'	16'
2'-8" x 6'-6"	16'	16'
2'-0" x 6'-8"	18'	16'
2'-4" x 6'-8"	18'	16'
2'-6" x 6'-8"	18'	16'
2'-8" x 6'-8"	18'	18'
3'-0" x 6'-8"	18'	18'
3'-6" x 6'-8"	18'	18'
4'-0" x 6'-8"	20'	18'
4'-6" x 6'-8"	20'	18'
5'-0" x 6'-8"	20'	20'
2'-0" x 7'-0"	18'	18'
2'-4" x 7'-0"	18'	18'
2'-6" x 7'-0"	18'	18'
2'-8" x 7'-0"	18'	18'
3'-0" x 7'-0"	18'	18'
3'-6" x 7'-0"	20'	18'
4'-0" x 7'-0"	20'	20'
4'-6" x 7'-0"	20'	20'
5'-0" x 7'-0"	20'	20'

To use the table:

1. Read the floor plan for the door size.
2. Select this size door in the table.
3. Read the number in column II or III which is the standard length of lumber to order to make the jamb, outside casing, or stop for that size door.

DOOR AND WINDOW AREA TABLE

When estimating some materials it is necessary to make deductions on account of openings in the walls. The following table gives the area of standard size door and window openings. For mullion or triple frames the combined area is based on the sizes of each window in the frame.

There are a number of estimating situations which require the estimator to know the area of the wall openings. When figuring siding, the quantity of stock needed is naturally affected by the size and number of doors and windows. This is also true when figuring wood shingle wall sheathing, and diagonal or storm sheathing.

The table will be found useful when applied to estimating the areas of brick walls or plastered surfaces. Its application is based on the trade practice followed, relative to wall openings. Experts in these fields should be consulted to learn the exact procedure as trade practices vary considerably when the problem arises concerning the deduction of wall areas because of the openings. Sometimes an opening is figured as though it were solid; the material saved is offset by the additional labor required to work around an opening. Estimating the surface as though it were solid will give the contractor a little leeway because of increased labor costs.

TABLE XXXII

DOOR AND WINDOW AREA TABLE

I. Doors

Size of Door	Area of Door in Square Feet*
2'-0" x 6'-6"	13
2'-0" x 6'-8"	13
2'-0" x 7'-0"	14
2'-4" x 6'-6"	15
2'-4" x 6'-8"	15
2'-4" x 7'-0"	16
2'-6" x 6'-6"	16
2'-6" x 6'-8"	16
2'-6" x 7'-0"	17
2'-8" x 6'-6"	17
2'-8" x 6'-8"	17
2'-8" x 7'-0"	18
3'-0" x 6'-8"	20
3'-0" x 7'-0"	21
3'-0" x 7'-6"	22
3'-6" x 6'-8"	23
3'-6" x 7'-0"	24
3'-6" x 7'-6"	26
4'-0" x 6'-8"	26
4'-0" x 7'-0"	28
4'-0" x 7'-6"	30

*Areas, as given, are reduced to the nearest whole foot.

II. Windows

Size of Window	Area of Window in Square Feet*
1'-6" x 3'-0"	4
1'-6" x 4'-0"	6
1'-6" x 4'-6"	6
1'-6" x 5'-1"	7
2'-0" x 3'-0"	6
2'-0" x 4'-0"	8
2'-0" x 4'-6"	9
2'-0" x -5'1"	10
2'-4" x -5'1"	11
2'-6" x 3-'0"	7
2'-6" x 4-'0"	10
2'-6" x 4'-6"	11
2'-6" x 5'-1"	12
3'-0" x 3'-0"	9
3'-0" x 4'-0"	12
3'-0" x 4'-6"	13
3'-0" x 5'-1"	15
3'-6" x 3'-0"	10
3'-6" x 4'-0"	14
3'-6" x 4'-6"	15
3'-6" x 5'-1"	17
4'-0" x 4'-0"	16
4'-0" x 4'-6"	18
4'-0" x 5'-1"	20

*Areas, as given, are reduced to the nearest whole foot.

III. Mullion Frames

Size of Frame	Area of Mullion Frame*
$\dfrac{1'\text{-}6'' \times 1'\text{-}6''}{3'\text{-}0''}$	9
$\dfrac{1'\text{-}6'' \times 1'\text{-}6''}{4'\text{-}0''}$	12
$\dfrac{1'\text{-}6'' \times 1'\text{-}6''}{4'\text{-}6''}$	13
$\dfrac{1'\text{-}6'' \times 1'\text{-}6''}{5'\text{-}1''}$	15
$\dfrac{2'\text{-}0'' \times 2'\text{-}0''}{3'\text{-}0''}$	12
$\dfrac{2'\text{-}0'' \times 2'\text{-}0''}{4'\text{-}0''}$	16
$\dfrac{2'\text{-}0'' \times 2'\text{-}0''}{4'\text{-}6''}$	18
$\dfrac{2'\text{-}0'' \times 2'\text{-}0''}{5'\text{-}1''}$	20
$\dfrac{2'\text{-}6'' \times 2'\text{-}6''}{3'\text{-}0''}$	15
$\dfrac{2'\text{-}6'' \times 2'\text{-}6''}{4'\text{-}0''}$	20
$\dfrac{2'\text{-}6'' \times 2'\text{-}6''}{4'\text{-}6''}$	22
$\dfrac{2'\text{-}6'' \times 2'\text{-}6''}{5'\text{-}1''}$	25
$\dfrac{3'\text{-}0'' \times 3'\text{-}0''}{3'\text{-}0''}$	18
$\dfrac{3'\text{-}0'' \times 3'\text{-}0''}{4'\text{-}0''}$	24
$\dfrac{3'\text{-}0'' \times 3'\text{-}0''}{4'\text{-}6''}$	27

*Areas, as given, are reduced to the nearest whole foot.

III. Mullion Frames (*Continued*)

Size of Frame	Area of Mullion Frame*
3'-0" x 3'-0" / 5'-1"	30
3'-6" x 3'-6" / 3'-0"	21
3'-6" x 3'-6" / 4'-0"	28
3'-6" x 3'-6" / 4'-6"	31
3'-6" x 3'-6" / 5'-1"	35
4'-0" x 4'-0" / 4'-0"	32
4'-0" x 4'-0" / 4'-6"	36
4'-0" x 4'-0" / 5'-1"	40
4'-6" x 4'-6" / 4'-0"	36
4'-6" x 4'-6" / 4'-6"	40
4'-6" x 4'-6" / 5'-1"	45
5'-0" x 5'-0" / 4'-0"	40
5'-0" x 5'-0" / 4'-6"	45
5'-0" x 5'-0" / 5'-1"	50

*Areas, as given, are reduced to the nearest whole foot.

IV. TRIPLET FRAMES

Size of Frame	Area of Triplet Frame*
$\dfrac{1'\text{-}6'' \times 1'\text{-}6'' \times 1'\text{-}6''}{3'\text{-}0''}$	13
$\dfrac{1'\text{-}6'' \times 1'\text{-}6'' \times 1'\text{-}6''}{4'\text{-}0''}$	18
$\dfrac{1'\text{-}6'' \times 1'\text{-}6'' \times 1'\text{-}6''}{4'\text{-}6''}$	20
$\dfrac{1'\text{-}6'' \times 1'\text{-}6'' \times 1'\text{-}6''}{5'\text{-}1''}$	24
$\dfrac{2'\text{-}0'' \times 2'\text{-}0'' \times 2'\text{-}0''}{3'\text{-}0''}$	18
$\dfrac{2'\text{-}0'' \times 2'\text{-}0'' \times 2'\text{-}0''}{4'\text{-}0''}$	24
$\dfrac{2'\text{-}0'' \times 2'\text{-}0'' \times 2'\text{-}0''}{4'\text{-}6''}$	27
$\dfrac{2'\text{-}0'' \times 2'\text{-}0'' \times 2'\text{-}0''}{5'\text{-}1''}$	30
$\dfrac{2'\text{-}6'' \times 2'\text{-}6'' \times 2'\text{-}6''}{3'\text{-}0''}$	22
$\dfrac{2'\text{-}6'' \times 2'\text{-}6'' \times 2'\text{-}6''}{4'\text{-}0''}$	30
$\dfrac{2'\text{-}6'' \times 2'\text{-}6'' \times 2'\text{-}6''}{4'\text{-}6''}$	34
$\dfrac{2'\text{-}6'' \times 2'\text{-}6'' \times 2'\text{-}6''}{5'\text{-}1''}$	38
$\dfrac{3'\text{-}0'' \times 3'\text{-}0'' \times 3'\text{-}0''}{3'\text{-}0''}$	27
$\dfrac{3'\text{-}0'' \times 3'\text{-}0'' \times 3'\text{-}0''}{4'\text{-}0''}$	36
$\dfrac{3'\text{-}0'' \times 3'\text{-}0'' \times 3'\text{-}0''}{4'\text{-}6''}$	40

*Areas, as given, are reduced to the nearest whole foot.

IV. Triplet Frames (*Continued*)

Size of Frame	Area of Triplet Frame*
3'-0" x 3'-0" x 3'-0" / 5'-1"	45
3'-6" x 3'-6" x 3'-6" / 3'-0"	31
3'-6" x 3'-6" x 3'-6" / 4'-0"	42
3'-6" x 3'-6" x 3'-6" / 4'-6"	47
3'-6" x 3'-6" x 3'-6" / 5'-1"	53
4'-0" x 4'-0" x 4'-0" / 4'-0"	48
4'-0" x 4'-0" x 4'-0" / 4'-6"	54
4'-0" x 4'-0" x 4'-0" / 5'-1"	61

*Areas, as given, are reduced to the nearest whole foot.

To use the above table, proceed as follows:

1. Read the floor plan carefully and make a list of all openings shown. The accepted trade practice followed is to read the plan "counter-clockwise," starting at the front door, listing all openings as they occur. For the interior openings read the horizontal partitions first; then go across the plan in the other direction, or *vice versa*.

2. Find these sizes in the table. Read and list the area of each.

3. Figure the total area of the wall.

4. Deduct from the total area combined area of openings as found in step 2.

SASH WEIGHT TABLES

The following table indicates the approximate weight of a number of standard size glazed windows. To accurately balance a double hung window, each sash should be weighed and then the weights ordered accordingly. The difference in the thickness of the glass, or the kind of lumber used, will make some difference in the exact weight of each sash. One-half pound sash washers can be bought to help secure a good smooth balance.

The weights given are for both upper and lower sash of a double hung window. Each sash requires two weights. Dividing the weight of a complete double hung window by 4 will give the correct size sash weight to order.

NOTE: It is not common practice today to specify sash weights and sash cord for residential work . This is due to the use of narrow trim which does not permit a weight pocket wide enough for the weight to slide freely and also because of the increased use of sash balances. There are a number of types of sash balances available. However, when repairs are made on a residence the usual procedure is to make the new work conform in general to the old; when this is done then sash weights are necessary.

In public buildings sash weights are usually specified to be hung on sash chain due to its durability and the necessity for using a balance that will stand hard use.

TABLE XXXIII
SASH WEIGHT TABLE

Size of Window			Window	Sash Weight
Width	Length	Thickness	Pounds	Pounds
1'-6"	3'-0"	1⅜	10 lbs.	2½ lbs.
1'-6"	4'-0"	1⅜	12 lbs.	3 lbs.
1'-6"	4'-6"	1⅜	14 lbs.	3½ lbs.
1'-6"	5'-0"	1⅜	14 lbs.	3½ lbs.
2'-0"	3'-0"	1⅜	14 lbs.	3½ lbs.
2'-0"	4'-0"	1⅜	16 lbs.	4 lbs.
2'-0"	4'-6"	1⅜	18 lbs.	4½ lbs.
2'-0"	5'-1"	1⅜	20 lbs.	5 lbs.
2'-4"	3'-0"	1⅜	16 lbs.	4 lbs.
2'-4"	4'-0"	1⅜	20 lbs.	5 lbs.
2'-4"	5'-1"	1⅜	22 lbs.	5½ lbs.
2'-6"	3'-0"	1⅜	16 lbs.	4 lbs.
2'-6"	4'-0"	1⅜	20 lbs.	5 lbs.
2'-6"	4'-6"	1⅜	22 lbs.	5½ lbs.
2'-6"	5'-1"	1⅜	24 lbs.	6 lbs.
3'-0"	3'-0"	1⅜	18 lbs.	4½ lbs.
3'-0"	4'-0"	1⅜	22 lbs.	5½ lbs.
3'-0"	4'-6"	1⅜	24 lbs.	6 lbs.
3'-0"	5'-1"	1⅜	28 lbs.	7 lbs.
3'-6"	3'-0"	1⅜	22 lbs.	5½ lbs.
3'-6"	4'-0"	1⅜	26 lbs.	6½ lbs.
3'-6"	4' 6"	1⅜	28 lbs.	7 lbs.
3'-6"	5'-1"	1⅜	30 lbs.	7½ lbs.
4'-0"	4'-0"	1⅜	28 lbs.	7 lbs.
4'-0"	5'-1"	1⅜	30 lbs.	7½ lbs.
4'-0"	4'-6"	1⅜	34 lbs.	8½ lbs.

To use the table, proceed as follows:
1. Select the correct size window.
2. Read the weight of this size window.
3. Divide this figure by 4. Result is size weight to order.
4. Order four of this size for each window.

TABLE OF NAIL SIZES

The following table indicates the approximate number of nails in a pound for a variety of sizes.

TABLE XXXIV

SIZES OF STANDARD STEEL WIRE NAILS

Size	Length	Common	Box	Finish
	Inches	Approx. No. per Pound	Approx. No. per Pound	Approx No. per Pound
2d	1	876	1010	1351
3d	1¼	568	635	807
4d	1½	316	473	584
5d	1¾	271	406	500
6d	2	181	236	309
7d	2¼	161	210	238
8d	2½	106	145	189
9d	2¾	96	132	172
10d	3	69	94	121
12d	3¼	63	88	113
16d	3½	49	71	90
20d	4	31	52	62
30d	4½	24	—	—
40d	5	18	—	—
50d	5½	14	—	—
60d	6	11	—	—

TABLE OF NAIL QUANTITIES

The following table indicates the size and the number of pounds necessary for fastening some of the important parts of a house. Trade practice varies in different parts of the country regarding the number and size nails used.

TABLE XXXV

NAIL QUANTITIES

I Name of Material	II Quantity of Material	III Lbs. Re- quired	IV Size	V Kind
Wall Studs (Includes nails in top late). No openings.	100 pcs.	13 lbs. 5 lbs.	8d 16d	common common
Framed opening	10 average openings	1½ lbs. 8 lbs.	8d 16d	common common
Bottom plate or Doubling plate	1000 lin. ft.	25 lbs.	16d	common
Sub-floor	1000 sq. ft. floor area	30 lbs.	8d	box
1″ x 4″ Sheathing	1000 bd. ft.	35 lbs.	8d	common
1″ x 6″ Sheathing	1000 bd. ft.	22 lbs.	8d	common
Rafters	for 1000 sq. ft. floor area	9 lbs. 6 lbs.	8d 16d	common common
1″ x 4″ Pine flooring	1000 bd. ft.	20 lbs.	8d	box
10″ Siding	1000 bd. ft.	15 lbs.	8d	box
8″ Siding	1000 bd. ft.	12 lbs.	6d	box
6″ Siding	1000 bd. ft.	8 lbs.	6d	box
4″ Siding	1000 bd. ft.	12 lbs.	6d	box
Baseboard, 4″, 6″ or 8″ widths	1000 lin. ft.	5 lbs.	6d	finish
Inside casings 3″ to 6″ widths and ¾″ thick	1000 lin. ft.	6 lbs. 4 lbs.	8d 6d	finish finish
Shingles, wood	1000	3 lbs.	3d	galvanized

To use the table:

1. Figure the quantities of material required for the job.
2. Divide the quantity of material by the measuring unit in Column II.
3. Multiply this result by the number of pounds required, as given in Column III. The result will be the number of pounds of nails to order.
4. State on the order the size and kind of nails as given in Columns IV and V.

CHAPTER VIII

ESTIMATING SHORT CUTS

A CARPENTER IS OFTEN called upon to make preliminary estimates and needs to know *approximately* how many board feet of lumber will be required for a job.

The following tables can be used as a short cut method to determine this board footage. The constants in the tables are based on average construction, they will *not* apply to special framing situations.

The use of the tables is based on the assumption a check-up sheet similar to the one illustrated on page 5 will be used. All areas needed will have been pre-determined on this sheet.

Trade judgment will indicate, after a little practice, the accuracy of the results obtained by using the short cuts. Any special, out of the ordinary feature, which may be called for on the plans, will have to be estimated by the regular detailed take off method.

Each sub-division of the framing lumber table includes "variables" which must be itemized and added to the board footage found by using the different constants listed.

TABLE XXXVI*

FRAMING LUMBER SHORT CUTS

I. UNDERPINNING UNIT

The parts of the underpinning unit are all "variables" as foundations differ greatly due to architect's details

*Table XXXVI is in six parts, pages 177-182 inclusive.

and construction methods; the slope of the lot; the kind of soil and building ordinance requirements.

I. Underpinning Unit

There is no short cut rule which can be written for the underpinning unit.

Parts: Mudsill, pierblocks, posts, girders, cribbing studs.

Variables: All items.

II. FLOOR UNIT

The floor unit short cut table is in two parts, namely, joists and sub-floor. The constants given represent *the number of board feet of lumber per square foot* of floor area.

II. Floor Unit

JOISTS

Parts: Floor joists, header joists, doubling joists, fireplace headers, solid blocking, bridging and sub-floor.

Joist Size (16″ o. c.)	2x6	2x8	2x10	2x12
Board Feet per Square Foot of Floor Area	.8	1.1	1.35	1.6

Variables: Header joists, doubling joists, fireplace headers, solid blocking and bridging.

There are a number of "variables" in the floor unit. Bridging is only used when wide joist spans are necessary, such as over a basement; the number of doubling joists depends on the number of bearing partitions; fireplace headers are naturally required only when the plans call for a fireplace, and the linear feet of header joists depends on the way the joists are laid. The number of linear feet of solid blocking depends on the architect's construction drawings and the building ordinance.

Rule: Floor area $\times$ constant equals board feet of lumber. Then add the board feet of lumber in the "variables."

SUB-FLOOR

The short cut rule for sub-floors is no different than the regular sub-floor take-off rules. Therefore, see table IX, page 42.

III. WALL UNIT

The lumber in an ordinary framed wall will not vary a great deal for each 100 square feet of wall area, except as the stud sizes change, even though some walls have more openings than others and some openings are larger than others. Different wall heights require different constants.

III. WALL UNIT

Parts: Plates, studs, braces, firestops, backing, storm sheathing, topheaders.

Stud Size (16" o. c.)	2x4	2x4	2x6	2x6
Ceiling Height	8'	9'	8'	9'
Board Feet per Square Foot of Wall Area	1.25	1.32	1.87	2.00

Variables: Storm sheathing and top headers.

There are two "variables" to be considered, namely diagonal or storm sheathing, as many buildings are not sheathed, and top headers which will vary in size and number.

Rule: Wall area $\times$ constant equals board feet of lumber; then add the variables.

NOTE: For an 8' garage wall multiply wall area by .0107.

IV. CEILING UNIT

Ceiling joists are usually 2 x 4 or 2 x 6 and placed 16" o.c. The constant table follows:

IV. CEILING UNIT

Parts: Joists, stiffeners, backing, bridging.

Joist Size (16" o. c.)	2x4	2x6	2x8	2x10
Board Feet per Square Foot of Area	.72	1.00	1.32	1.60

Variables: Ceiling backing, and bridging.

The "variables" in the ceiling unit are ceiling backing, which varies according to the number of cross partitions in the job, and bridging.

Rule: Area $\times$ constant equals board feet of lumber. Then add the board feet of lumber in the ceiling backing and bridging.

V. ROOF UNIT

The quantity of lumber varies according to the shape of the roof, the size of the rafter stock and the kind of roofing used. It is difficult to obtain a very accurate estimate of the number of board feet of lumber in a roof, but the following table will give a fairly close answer.

To find the area of a roof proceed as follows:

1. If the building has no cornice multiply the width and length dimensions together and deduct the "take-away" areas. See figure 17, page 42. If there is a cornice add twice the cornice run to the building measurements before multiplying.
2. Read the blueprint and find the roof pitch.
3. Select a constant in table XI, page 61, which corresponds to the roof pitch.
4. Multiply the areas as found in step 1 by the constant; the result will be the pitch area of the roof.

V. ROOF UNIT

GABLE ROOF

Parts: Rafters, sheathing, purline, braces, gable studs.

a. Wood Shingle Roof: 1x4 Sheathing		
Rafter Size (24″ o. c.)	2x4	2x6
Board Feet of Lumber per Square Foot of Area	1.15	1.35

b. Composition Roofing: 1x6 Sheathing		
Rafter Size (24″ o. c.)	2x4	2x6
Board Feet of Lumber per Square Foot of Area	1.65	1.85

Variables: None.

Rule: Roof area $\times$ constant equals board feet of lumber.

HIP ROOF

Add 10% to above results for a hip roof.

VI. ENTIRE FRAME (all above units)

A quick short cut rule for all framing lumber for an average one story residence is as follows:

VI. ENTIRE FRAME (all above units)*

Board Feet Per Square Foot of Floor Area	8 or 8.5

Storm sheathing not included.

Rule: Floor area $\times$ constant equals board feet.

NOTE: 8½ is used when there are one or two 2 x 6 partitions or one or two double walls. It should again be emphasized that all results obtained by using the constants in table XXXVI are approximate only, and are based on *ordinary* construction.

Before using either 8 or 8½ the plans and specifications should be checked and any special construction item which requires extra materials above ordinary requirements should be listed. These "extras" are then converted to board feet and added to the total obtained by using either constant.

A careful check-up after a job is completed, of all the lumber delivery tickets, to determine the actual number of board feet of lumber used, is always worthwhile and considered excellent estimating procedure. These totals should then be compared with the total obtained by using one of the "entire frame" constants given above. Check-ups of this character will indicate the accuracy of this rule.

FINISH LUMBER SHORT CUTS

There are a number of building units requiring *finish* lumber which can be estimated on a short cut basis. These include door and window frames, inside trim for these frames, inside trim for inside doors and, lastly, drawers and cabinets. Each of these units is discussed in the following pages and is included in Table XXXVII.

The constants in this table were developed as follows:

1. The number of board feet of lumber required for *one linear foot of the building item* described in each part of the table was figured first. This was done by listing the various parts, considering each to be 12″ in length and then reducing all to board feet.

2. This result (or constant) was then multiplied by the length of the material required to make the item. See table XXX, page 163 and table XXXI, page 164.

3. The result equaled the approximate number of board feet of lumber to order per unit.

Experience gained through carefully recording the amount of lumber used for the various building items requiring finish lumber, after they have been *constructed on the job,* will verify the closeness of the board footage constants in the various parts of the table. It is not possible to give an exact figure but for all practical purposes the amounts are fairly accurate.

The final result *cannot* be used as the basis for ordering the lumber to be delivered to the job but it will serve as a practical estimate. Much time is saved over the longer method of listing the exact materials and giving the necessary thickness, width and length dimensions. Cutting lists are *only* required if and when a contract is secured and then are made out by the carpenter foreman. This short cut method is recommended for use only if the estimator is familiar with the *details* pertaining to taking off material bills.

TABLE XXXVII*

FINISH LUMBER SHORT CUTS

1. DOUBLE-HUNG AND CASEMENT WINDOW FRAMES

The following table is based on using standard construction as indicated in figure 72. It can be used for any frame which is similarly made as the cross section of any standard window frame for a 2″ x 4″ wall, of necessity, will only include about the same amount of lumber. The total footage includes the sill which has been figured as 2″ x 8″ stock. If 1″ x 5″ casing is used instead of 1¼″ x 1¼″ moulding use the constants in the column which covers this type of construction.

Note: No apron has been included as many buildings require none, particularly if the exterior walls are plastered. If the design o fa building necessitates an apron it can be easily figured as the estimator only needs to find the combined width of all frames; then add from 6″ to 12″ per frame, depending on the width of the casing stock, and convert the total linear feet of material to board feet. See page 119. This total is then added into

*Table XXXVII is in 6 parts, pages 184-201 inclusive.

the totals found by using the constants given in the table above.

To use the table proceed as follows:

1. Make a list of all the frames required for the job.
2. Select from the table the constants which represent the board footage of lumber for various sizes of

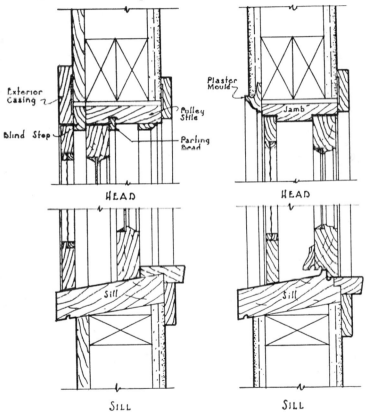

FIG. 72—*Section Through Casement and Double-Hung Window Frame*

1. DOUBLE-HUNG AND CASEMENT
WINDOW FRAMES

Pulley Stile   1″ x 5″   Parting bead . . 3/8″ x 3/4″
Blind Stop . . 1″ x 2″   Sill . . . . 2″ x 8″
Moulding . . 1¼″ x 1¼″ . . . or . . . . Casing . . . . . . 1″ x 5″

Size of Frame	Total Footage*	
	Using Plaster Mould	Using 1″ x 5″ Casing
1′-6″ x 2′-0″	10	11½
2′-0″ x 2′-0″	10	11½
2′-6″ x 2′-6″	11	13
3′-6″ x 2′-6″	15	17½
1′-6″ x 3′-0″	12	14
2′-0″ x 3′-0″	12	14
2′-6″ x 3′-0″	14	16½
3′-0″ x 3′-0″	15	17½
3′-6″ x 3′-0″	17	20
2′-0″ x 3′-6″	13	15½
3′-0″ x 3′-6″	17	20
3′-6″ x 3′-6″	17	20
1′-6″ x 4′-0″	15	18
2′-0″ x 4′-0″	15	18
2′-6″ x 4′-0″	16	19
3′-0″ x 4′-0″	17	20
3′-6″ x 4′-0″	19	22
4′-0″ x 4′-0″	20	23
1′-6″ x 4′-6″	15	18
2′-0″ x 4′-6″	15	18
2′-6″ x 4′-6″	18	21
1′-6″ x 5′-1″	17	20
2′-0″ x 5′-1″	17	20
2′-6″ x 5′-1″	18	21
3′-0″ x 5′-1″	21	25
4′-0″ x 5′-1″	22	26

*For casement frames using 1¼″ rabbetted stock use constants as given above. If a 1″ x 6″ jamb is used with a ½″ x 3″ stop add 1 foot to *each constant.*

frames. Check the blueprint to see if $1\frac{1}{4}''$ plaster moulding is required or $1'' \times 5''$ casing stock.

3. Multiply each constant by the number of window frames having the same dimensions.

4. Add up the footage for each group of frames. Result equals total footage of lumber required which is now estimated at the *average* price of the different kinds of lumber specified. In nearly every case only one price need be considered, as finish lumber for window frames will not vary much per M board feet even though several kinds of material are required.

II. EXTERIOR DOOR FRAMES (Includes threshold)

Figure 73 indicates the type of construction used when developing the following table. Lumber footage is the same if $1\frac{1}{4}''$ rabbetted stock is used but no stop. Sometimes oak is specified for door sills, therefore the total footage in the third column has been adjusted to allow for this kind of lumber. The constant in this column is to be considered as though all of the lumber were pine as the increased footage allows for the increased cost of oak over pine. To illustrate: A $3'-0''$ door frame requires 5 board feet of sill. This was increased to 15 board feet when computing the constants in the third column as oak costs about three times as much as pine.

While thresholds actually belong to the inside finish unit they are allowed for in the table to simplify the take-off work. The constants in all columns have therefore been adjusted to cover oak lumber, the same as was done for the door sills, since thresholds are always made of hardwood.

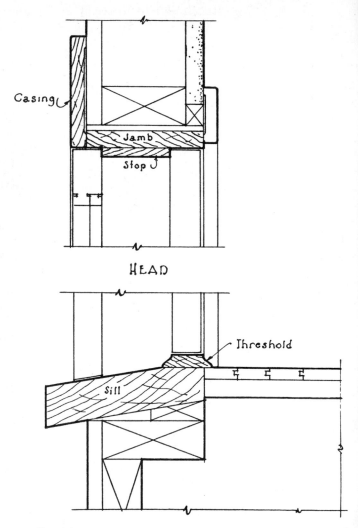

FIG. 73—*Section Through Exterior Door Frame*

II. EXTERIOR DOOR FRAMES

Jamb............ 1″ x 6″ or 1¼″ x 6″
Stop............. ½″ x 4″
Moulding........ 1¼″ x 1¼″ (or 1″ x 5″)*
Sill.............. 2″ x 8″
Oak threshold.... ⅝″ x 4″

Size of Frame	Total Footage Pine Sill		Total Footage Adjusted for Oak Sill	
	1″ Jamb	1¼″ Jamb	1″ Jamb	1¼″ Jamb
2′-0″ x 6′-6″	22	24½	28	30
2′-4″ x 6′-6″	23	25	31	33
2′-6″ x 6′-6″	23	25	31	33
2′-8″ x 6′-6″	24	26	34	36
2′-0″ x 6′-8″	24½	27	30½	33
2′-4″ x 6′-8″	26	28½	34	36½
2′-6″ x 6′-8″	26	28½	34	36½
2′-8″ x 6′-8″	27	29½	37	39½
3′-0″ x 6′-8″	27½	30	37½	40
3′-6″ x 6′-8″	28	30½	38	40½
4′-0″ x 6′-8″	31½	34½	43½	46½
4′-6″ x 6′-8″	32	35	46	49
5′-0″ x 6′-8″	33½	36½	49½	52½
2′-0″ x 7′-0″	24½	27	30½	33
2′-4″ x 7′-0″	26	28½	34	36½
2′-6″ x 7′-0″	26	28½	34	36½
2′-8″ x 7′-0″	27	29½	37	39½
3′-0″ x 7′-0″	27½	30	37½	40
3′-6″ x 7′-0″	30	33	40	43
4′-0″ x 7′-0″	31½	34½	43½	46½
4′-6″ x 7′-0″	33	36	47	50
5′-0″ x 7′-0″	34½	37½	50½	53½

*If 1″ x 5″ casing stock is used instead of the 1¼″ x 1¼″ plaster mould-
ing add 4 feet to *each* constant.

To use the table proceed as follows:

1. Make a list of all the exterior doors in the job grouping by similar dimensions.
2. Select from the table the constants which represent board footage of lumber for the various sizes of frames. Be sure to consult the plans to see which frames require oak sills and whether plaster moulding or casing stock is specified.
3. Add up the footage for each group of exterior frames, results equal amount of lumber to place on the estimate sheet.

III. INSIDE TRIM FOR EXTERIOR DOORS

Inside trim for an exterior door frame pertains only to the casing required to cover the joint between the

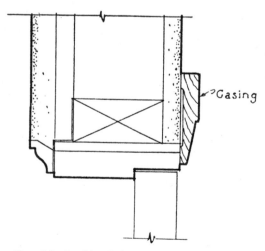

FIG. 74—*Inside Trim for Exterior Doors*

plaster and the back edge of the frame jamb. See figure 74. It can be accurately estimated on a board footage basis as it is easy to determine the number of board feet of lumber per linear foot of jamb.

III. INSIDE TRIM FOR EXTERIOR DOORS*

Size of Door	Width of Casing				
	1" x 2"	1" x 3"	1" x 4"	1" x 5"	1" x 6"
2'-0" x 6'-6" 2'-4" x 6'-6" 2'-6" x 6'-6" 2'-8" x 6'-6"	3	4	5½	7	8
2'-0" x 6'-8" 2'-4" x 6'-8" 2'-6" x 6'-8" 2'-8" x 6'-8" 3'-0" x 6'-8" 3'-6" x 6'-8"	3	4½	6	7½	9
4'-0" x 6'-8" 4'-6" x 6'-8" 5'-0" x 6'-8"	3½	5	7	8½	10
2'-0" x 7'-0" 2'-4" x 7'-0" 2'-6" x 7'-0" 2'-8" x 7'-0" 3'-0" x 7'-0"	3	4½	6	7½	9
3'-6" x 7'-0" 4'-0" x 7'-0" 4'-6" x 7'-0" 5'-0" x 7'-0"	3½	5	7	8½	10

*All constants have been increased to half or whole feet to simplify the mathematical process.

The shape of the casing does not affect the number of board feet of lumber required to make it as all inside finish material which has been milled to the design required is always figured on the basis of the rough sizes of the original stock before it was machined.

Threshold material is not included in the following table as this item is most easily figured (on a short cut basis) with the door frame and has, therefore, been included in part II above.

To use the table proceed as follows:

1. List the exterior doors required for the job.
2. Read the blueprints and specifications to determine width of casing specified.
3. Select from the table the total footage of inside trim required for each different size door, based on the width of the casing.
4. Multiply this constant by the number of doors having the same dimensions.
5. Combine the footage of the different size frames. Result equals total inside trim lumber footage to place on the estimate.

IV. INSIDE TRIM FOR WINDOW FRAMES

The following table is similar to the exterior door frame table above. It is likewise based on the different width interior casings most generally used in modern house construction. The stool and apron material is not included in the constant as the board feet of finish lumber for this item varies according to the width of the frame. The rule for stool and apron is to *allow one board foot of finish lumber for each foot of frame width*. See figure 75.

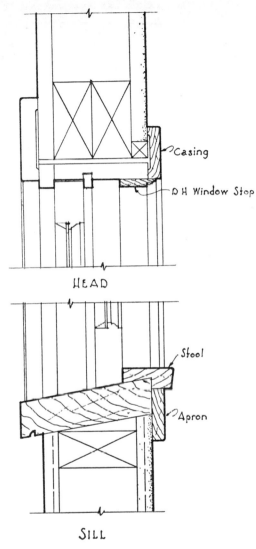

HEAD

SILL

FIG. 75—*Inside Trim for Window Frame*

I. INSIDE TRIM FOR WINDOW FRAMES*

Size of Window	Width of Casing					
	1"x2"	1"x3"	1"x4"	1"x5"	1"x6"	
1'-6" x 2'-0" 2'-0" x 2'-0" 2'-0" x 2'-6"	1½	2	3	3½	4	"a"
3'-6" x 2'-6" 1'-6" x 3'-0" 2'-0" x 3'-0" 2'-6" x 3'-0" 3'-0" x 3'-0"	2	2½	3½	4½	5	"b"
3'-6" x 3'-0" 2'-0" x 3'-6" 3'-0" x 3'-6" 3'-6" x 3'-6" 1'-6" x 4'-0" 2'-0" x 4'-0" 2'-6" x 4'-0" 3'-0" x 4'-0"	2	3	4	5	6	"c"
3'-6" x 4'-0" 4'-0" x 4'-0" 1'-6" x 4'-6" 2'-0" x 4'-6" 2'-6" x 4'-6" 1'-6" x 5'-1" 2'-0" x 5'-1" 2'-6" x 5'-1" 3'-0" x 5'-1"	2½	3½	5	6	7	"d"
4'-0" x 5'-1"	3	4	5½	7	8	"e"

*All constants have been increased to half or whole feet to simplify the mathematical process.

For a *double hung window* additional material is needed for the inside window stop, which is usually ⅜″ x 1½″. (See figure 55, page 115.) Therefore, if inside trim for double hung windows is being estimated add to *each* constant the following amounts: group "a", 1½ feet; group "b", 2 feet; group "c", 2 feet; group "d", 2½ feet, and group "e", 3 feet.

To use the table proceed as follows:

1. List the window frames required for the job.
2. Read blueprints and specifications to determine casing width.
3. Select from the table the total footage of inside trim for each of the different sizes of frames, based on the width of the casing specified.
4. Multiply each constant selected by the number of units having the same dimensions.
5. For the stool and apron figure the total *combined* width of all window frames and allow one board foot of lumber for each linear foot of width.
6. Combine all totals developed in above steps. Result equals total board feet of inside finish lumber to place on the estimate.

V. INSIDE TRIM FOR INSIDE DOORS

In the following table the term "inside trim" has a wider definition than given to it when applied to window and door frames. The board foot constants cover the door jamb, casings for both edges of the jamb and the door stop. See figure 76. The constants are based on using 1″ finish lumber. If 1¼″ jambs are specified then use the rule given below the table.

If hardwood lumber is specified for some of the door trim, such as the openings in a living room or dining room, then these door openings should be listed sepa-

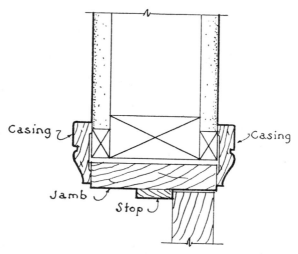

FIG. 76—*Section Through an Inside Door Jamb*

rately. Lumber footage for various building items cannot be combined if two or more kinds of lumber, which vary greatly in price, are specified.

To use the table proceed as follows:

1. List the inside doors required for the job. If hardwood is specified for certain doors make two lists.

2. Read the blueprints to determine the width of casings specified and how thick the jamb stock is to be.

V. INSIDE TRIM FOR INSIDE DOORS

Jamb stock 1" x 6"   Door stop 3/8" x 1 1/2"

Size of Door	Width of Casing				
	1" x 2"	1" x 3"	1" x 4"	1" x 5"	1" x 6"
2'-0" x 6'-6" 2'-4" x 6'-6" 2'-6" x 6'-6" 2'-8" x 6'-6"	18	20	23	26	28
2'-0" x 6'-8" 2'-4" x 6'-8" 2'-6" x 6'-8" 2'-8" x 6'-8" 3'-0" x 6'-8" 3'-6" x 6'-8"	20	23	26	29	32
4'-0" x 6'-8" 4'-6" x 6'-8" 5'-0" x 6'-8"	22	25	29	32	35
2'-0" x 7'-0" 2'-4" x 7'-0" 2'-6" x 7'-0" 2'-8" x 7'-0" 3'-0" x 7'-0"	20	23	26	29	32
3'-6" x 7'-0" 4'-0" x 7'-0" 4'-6" x 7'-0" 5'-0" x 7'-0"	22	25	29	32	35

*For 1 1/4" jamb stock add 2 1/2 board feet to *each* constant given in the table.

3. If the jamb stock is 1", select from the table above the constant which represents the total footage of inside trim lumber for each different size door

shown on the list. If 1¼″ jamb stock is specified add 2½ feet to *each* constant.

4. Multiply each constant selected by the number of inside doors having the same dimensions.

5. Combine the footage of the different size doors. Result equals the total footage of inside finish lumber to be placed on the estimate sheet.

6. If hardwood finish lumber is required for some of the doors repeat process as given above and make a separate entry on the estimate sheet.

VI. DRAWER LUMBER

Although drawers for the inside cabinet work of a residence are not made to any standard size it is not difficult to estimate the amount of finish lumber necessary to make them.

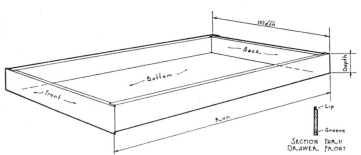

Fig. 77—*Illustrating Drawer Terms*

The table below indicates a number of drawers which are of average proportional dimensions such as will be found in most built-in cabinets.

The parts of a drawer included in the constants are front, sides, back and bottom. See figure 77. Drawer bottoms are usually 3 ply lumber but are figured in with the board feet of lumber required to make the sides, front and back in order to provide a short cut estimating method.

The term "run" refers to the drawer dimensions as measured from front to back. "Width" means the meas-

VI. DRAWER LUMBER

Drawer Sizes		Lumber Footage	
Width	Run	Depth	Board Feet
12″	24″	11″	8
15″	24″	3½″	5
		4½″	6
		5½″	7
		7¼″	8
		9″	9
		11″	10
18″	18″	3½″	5
		4½″	5
		5½″	6
		7¼″	7
		9″	8
		11″	9
24″	24″	3½″	7
		4½″	8
		5½″	8
		7¼″	10
		9″	11
		11″	12
36″	24″	5½″	11
		7¼″	13
		9″	15
		11	16
36″	36″	7¼″	17

urement from side to side; "depth" indicates how deep the drawer is on the *outside*. This measurement is usually based on the finished width of the drawer stock which can be bought already grooved to receive the bottom.

All constants have been increased to the next whole number.

To use the table proceed as follows:

1. List the different sizes of drawers required for the job.

2. Read the lumber footage given in the table for drawer sizes the same or nearest to the actual dimensions. Always select a larger rather than a smaller size.

3. Multiply the constant by the number of drawers required.

4. Combine the lumber footage for each size. Result equals total number of board feet of drawer lumber to list on the estimate sheet.

BASEBOARD, BASESHOE, HOOK STRIP AND PICTURE MOULDING

There is no short cut method to use when figuring baseboard, baseshoe, hookstrip and picture moulding. These items are all estimated on the basis of linear feet and the quantity of each depends on the number of rooms in the building and the dimensions of each. The rules on page 119-120 indicate how to determine the linear feet of each item.

Baseboard and hookstrip can be converted to board feet by using table XXVI, page 158. Baseshoe and picture moulding are converted to "moulding inches."*

SHORT CUTS FOR CABINET MATERIALS

A detailed estimate of the material required to construct a built-in cabinet necessitates that an itemized list of all of the parts be made. (See cabinet parts, page 151.) This job entails considerable estimating time as cabinets are rarely identical. Each one must be estimated as a separate item.

The estimating work can be simplified, however. Cabinets placed in certain rooms are designed according to a common need. To illustrate: sink cabinets are very much alike in all houses. Such a cabinet is generally 24" in depth and 36" high; the changing dimension is its length. Dish cupboards are usually 11" deep; linen closets are at least 24" deep so as to be large enough to receive bed linens, etc. See figures 78-86 inclusive.

These similarities of cabinet dimensions and designs make it possible to determine the "average" number of board feet of finish lumber necessary to construct them. The following table is based on these "averages". Nine cabinets are included, namely, kitchen sink, dish cupboard over the sink (sometimes known as a "hang" cabinet), kitchen cabinet and cooler, dish and drawer cabinet, broom cupboard, linen closet, medicine cabinet, book case and mantel shelf.

Drawers and cabinet doors are *not* included in the total lumber footage constants. They can be estimated independent of the cabinet, as cabinet doors are ordered and made to the exact sizes required and are ready to

---

*The meaning of the term "moulding inch" varies in different communities. Check with your lumber dealer.

hang when delivered; drawers likewise can be ordered made to the exact size required or, more often, are made on the job as a complete unit of work separate and apart from the cabinets which they are to fit.

To use the table proceed as follows:

1. Check the blueprints and make a list of the cabinets required. These should be listed by room locations grouping all cabinets for the same room.

2. Compare the blueprint detail of one of the cabinets with one of the illustrations in the table to determine similarity of design such as the number of drawers and doors, general over-all dimensions, etc.

3. If the cabinet to be estimated is similar, then select in the table, the board foot constants for cabinet which has approximately the same dimensions.

4. Continue for all other cabinets required for the job.

5. Add the board feet of lumber for each cabinet; result equals quantity of finish lumber to place on the estimate.

NOTE: It is not practical to *buy* the lumber for the cabinets on the board foot basis. A detailed list of material, of varying dimensions and lengths, will have to be made by the foreman carpenter of the job. He can take exact measurements of the various spaces into which the cabinets are to be built and order lumber which will cut with the least waste. The main advantage in using the short cut table is conservation of estimating time.

TABLE XXXVIII*

SHORT CUTS FOR CABINET MATERIALS

I. KITCHEN SINK CABINETS

SPECIFICATIONS

Kind of Lumber......Douglas Fir (or similar grade) S4S
and sanded

Cabinet Doors........1" net thick

Drawers.............Lip; center guide

End Jambs..........Four; full width; glued; also use corrugated fasteners

Shelf................Full width; glued; also use corrugated fasteners

Shelf Cleats..........1" x 2"

Bottom Shelf Supports 1" x 4"

Toe Strip............3" x 3"

Face Frame..........1¼" x 2" for hanging strips; top rail
or apron 1" x 6"

Rough Top..........1" x 6" S1S; to receive tile

LUMBER FOOTAGE REQUIRED

Cabinet Dimension			Board, feet of Lumber**
Length	Depth	Height	
8'	24"	36"	85
10'	24"	36"	100
12'	24"	36"	120
14'	24"	36"	140

*Table XXXVIII is in nine parts, pages 203-219, inclusive.
**No drawer lumber included. See page 198.

I. KITCHEN SINK CABINET—(Continued)

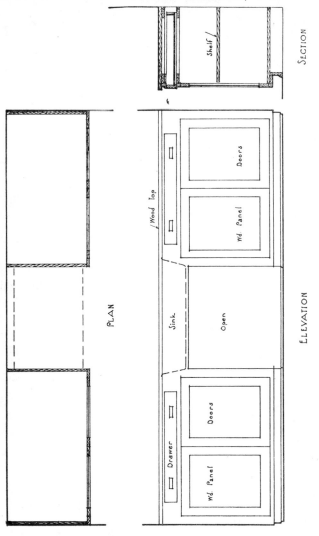

FIG. 78—A Kitchen Sink Cabinet

II. DISH CABINET (over sink)

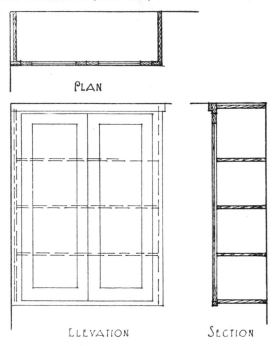

PLAN

ELEVATION   SECTION

FIG. 79– *A Dish Cabinet (Over Sink Cabinet)*

SPECIFICATIONS

Kind of Lumber . . . . . Douglas Fir (or similar grade) S4S and sanded

Jambs . . . . 1″ net thick

1″ x 12″ (to finish 11″ net) two required; exposed jamb to be scribed to wall

Shelves . . . . 1″ x 12″ (finish to 11″ net)

Shelf Cleats . . . . 1″ x 2″

Face Frame . . . . 1¼″ hanging stiles; 1¼″ x 6″ top rail

Cap Moulding . . . . 1¼″ x 2″ (at ceiling line)

LUMBER FOOTAGE REQUIRED

Cabinet Dimensions			Board Feet of Lumber
Depth	Width	Height	
12″	30″	48″	26
12″	36″	48″	29
12″	42″	48″	32
12″	48″	48″	35

III. KITCHEN CABINET AND COOLER

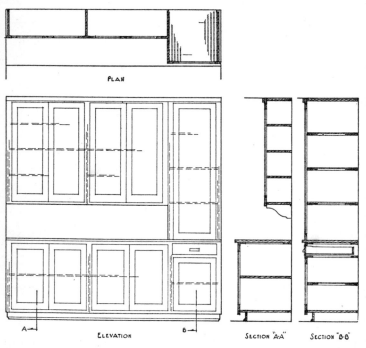

PLAN

ELEVATION

SECTION "A-A"

SECTION "B-B"

FIG. 80—*A Combination Kitchen Cabinet and Cooler*

SPECIFICATIONS

Kind of Lumber......Douglas Fir (or similar grade) S4S and sanded

Cabinet Doors.......1" net thick

Drawers.............Lip; center guide

Jambs...............*Cooler*: full width; glued

Lower cabinet: full width; glued; also use corrugated fastener

Upper cabinet: 1" x 2" (to finish 11" net)

Shelves.............*Lower Cabinet*: full width glued; also use corrugated fasteners

Upper cabinet: 1" x 12" (to finish 11" net)

Shelf Cleats.........1" x 2"

Bottom Shelf Supports 1" x 4"

Face Frame..........1¼" x 2"

Cooler Shelves.......1" x 2" frame; ⅜" x 1½" slats

LUMBER FOOTAGE REQUIRED

Cabinet Dimensions				Cooler Dimensions			
Depth lower	Depth upper	width	height	depth	width	height	B. F. lum.*
20"	12"	6'-0"	8'-4"	24"	24"	8'-4"	160
20"	12"	8'-0"	8'-4"	24"	24"	8'-4"	182

*NOTE: Allow 12 board feet of lumber for each additional linear foot of cabinet. (No drawer lumber is included.)

If mahogany counter shelf is specified add 24 board feet to 6' cabinet and 33 board feet for 8' cabinet. This increase allows for the difference in price of pine and mahogany.

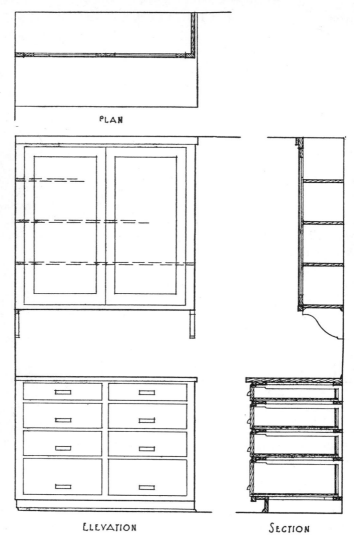

PLAN

ELEVATION SECTION

FIG. 81—*A Dish and Drawer Cabinet*

DISH AND DRAWER CABINET

SPECIFICATIONS

Kind of Lumber..... Douglas Fir (or similar qualtiy) S4S
and sanded

Cabinet Doors........1″ net thick

Drawers............. Lip; center guide

Jambs...............*Lower cabinet*: full width; glued;
also use corrugated fasteners

Upper cabinet: 1″ x 2″ (to finish
11″ net)

Shelves............ ... *Lower cabinet*: full width; glued

Upper cabinet: 1″ x 12″ (to finish
11″ net)

Bottom Shelf Supports.1″ x 2″

Shelf Cleats..........1″ x 4″

Face Frame..........*Lower cabinet*: 1″ x 2″

Upper cabinet: 1¼″ x 2″

LUMBER FOOTAGE REQUIRED

Cabinet Dimensions				Board Feet of Lumber*
Depth, lower	Depth, upper	Width	Height	
20″	12″	36″	8′-4″	72
20″	12″	48″	8′-4″	82

*NOTE: Add 10 board feet for each addtional foot of cabinet width.
No drawer lumber included. See page 198.

If mahognay counter shelf is specified add 12 board
feet to 36″ cabinet, 16 board feet to 48″ cabinet. This
increase allows for the difference in price of pine and
mahogany.

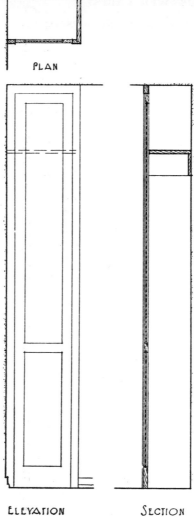

PLAN

ELEVATION   SECTION

FIG. 82—*A Broom Closet*

BROOM CLOSET

SPECIFICATIONS

Kind of Lumber..... Douglas Fir (or similar quality) S4S
sanded

Cabinet Door.........1″ net thick

Jamb................1″ x depth of closet and scribed to
wall. If over 12″ to be glued.

Shelf................1″ x depth of closet

Shelf Cleat...........1″ x 6″

Face Frame..........1¼″ x 2″

LUMBER FOOTAGE REQUIRED

Cabinet Dimensions			Board Feet of Lumber
Depth	Width	Height	
12″	18″	8′-4″	18
18″	18″	8′-4″	24
18″	24″	8′-4″	26
18″	36″	8′-4″	28
18″	48″	8′-4″	36

NOTE: Special hardware for holding brooms, mops, etc., can be secured at any hardware store. Check with your local hardware dealer. Some broom closet designs call for *two* doors; the joint between them centering on the shelf near the top of the cabinet. No increase in lumber is needed; the extra door will require additional hardware and labor to hang it.

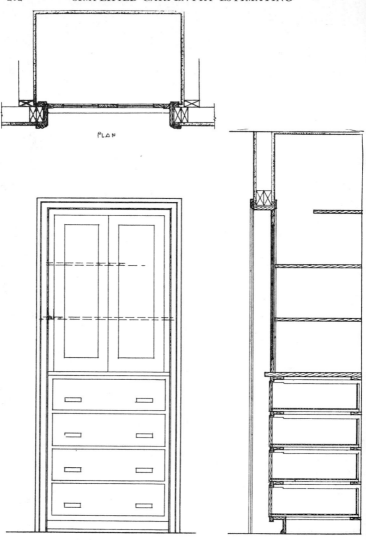

PLAN

ELEVATION   SECTION

Fig. 83—*A Linen Closet*

LINEN CLOSET

SPECIFICATIONS

Kind of Lumber . . . . . Douglas Fir (or similar quality) S4S and sanded

Drawers . . . . Lip; center guide

Cabinet Doors . . . . . . 1″ net thick

Jambs . . . . Use regular door jamb properly cased. Lumber for jambs and casings *not* included in the table below.

Shelves . . . . 1″ x full width; glued; also use corrugated fasteners

Shelf Cleats . . . . 1″ x 2″

Face Frame . . . . *Lower part*: 1″ x 2″
Upper part: 1¼″ x 2″

Bottom of Closet
(below drawers) . . Use either piece of shelf stock or ¼″ plywood to cover sub floor and make closet tight

LUMBER FOOTAGE REQUIRED

Closet Dimension			No. Shelves	No. Drawers	Board Feet of Lumber*
Depth	Width	Height			
24″	30″	6′-8″	3	4	36
24″	36″	6′-8″	3	4	40

*No drawer lumber included. See page 198.

VII. MEDICINE CABINET

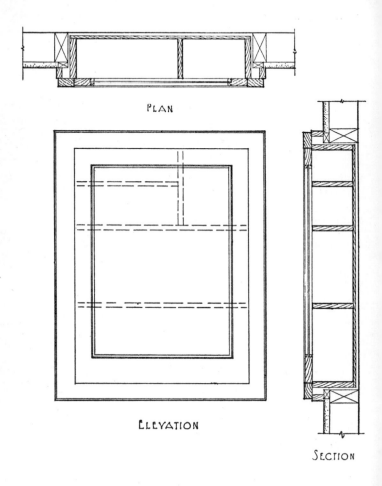

PLAN

ELEVATION

SECTION

FIG. 84—*A Built-in Medicine Cabinet*

SPECIFICATIONS

Kind of Lumber...... White pine (or similar quality) S4S and sanded

Cabinet Door........ 1″ net thick

Jambs.............. 1″ x 6″

Shelves............. 5/8″ x 5″

Shelf Cleats......... None; shelves grooved into jambs

Face Frame......... 1¼″ x ″2 (built out if cabinet is 6″ deep)

Back............... ¼″—3 ply paneling

This lumber footage table can be applied to a soap cabinet sometimes designed to go above a laundry tray as both cabinets approximate the same dimensions.

LUMBER FOOTAGE REQUIRED

Cabinet Dimensions			Board Feet of Lumber
Depth	Width	Height	
6″	18″	24″	12
6″	24″	30″	18
4″	18″	24″	10
4″	24″	30″	15

NOTE: A metal medicine cabinet with plate mirror door can be purchased as a complete unit ready for installation. These cabinets vary in price according to dimensions; local dealers should be consulted.

VIII. BOOKCASE

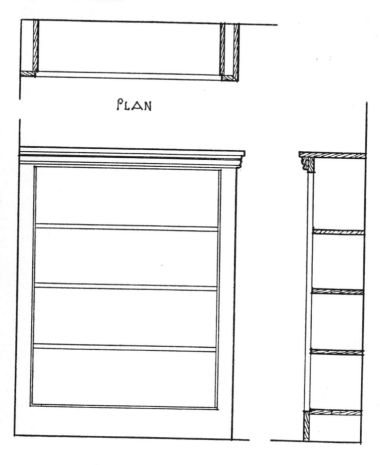

PLAN

ELEVATION   SECTION

FIG. 85—*A Bookcase*

SPECIFICATIONS

Kind of Lumber . . . . . Douglas Fir (or equal quality) S4S and sanded

Cabinet Doors . . . . . . None (front is constructed so that doors can be hung)

Jambs . . . . 1" x 8" net. Double jamb at exposed end of bookcase to permit a flush finish on the inside of the cabinet.

Shelves . . . . Three, 1" x 8" net; adjustable; to rest on adjustable shelf brackets. See Fig 70, page 142.

Face Frame . . . . 1¼" x 2"

Cap Moulding . . . . 1¼" x 2"

Back . . . . None

LUMBER FOOTAGE REQUIRED

Cabinet Dimensions			Board Feet of Lumber*
Depth	Width	Height	
8" net	36"	48"	30
8" net	48"	48"	36

*Note: Allow 6 board feet of lumber for each foot of additional width.

Before constructing any built-in bookcase the owner should be consulted regarding the sizes of his books and, if possible, the depth of the bookcase should be adjusted accordingly.

IX. MANTEL SHELF

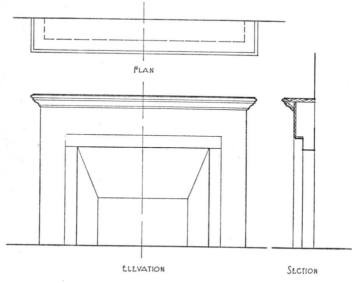

PLAN

ELEVATION   SECTION

FIG. 86—*A Mantel Shelf*

SPECIFICATIONS

Kind of Lumber..... Douglas Fir (or equal quality) S4S and sanded

Jambs............... *Ends*: 1″ x 8″ net (mitered to front jamb)

Front: 1″ x 18″; also 1″ x 24″ over opening

Cap Moulding....... 1″ x 4″

Shelf................ 1″ x 12″

LUMBER FOOTAGE REQUIRED

Dimensions of Mantel Shelf				Board Feet of Lumber Required*
Width of Fireplace	Height	Width of Ends	Width of Shelf	
6'-0"	4'-6"	8"	10"	45

*Footage allows for only one moulding which is under shelf. If more than one moulding is specified additional lumber will be required.

FACE FRAME LUMBER FOOTAGE CONSTANTS

The face frame of a cabinet consists of the hanging stiles and rails which form the door opening and the rails and vertical pieces which form the opening into

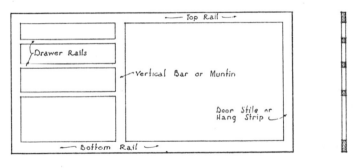

ELEVATION   SECTION

FIG. 87—*Illustrating Parts of a Cabinet Face Frame*

which a drawer will fit. See figure 87. The lumber is usually 1″ for the drawer face frame and 1¼″ for the door face frame although on small cabinets the front is often made from ¾" stock and the doors made the same thickness.

It is sometimes necessary for the estimator to compute the lumber footage in a face frame. Usually the pieces vary in width and are of several different lengths.

The following table gives the decimal board foot constant for each linear foot of a number of standard sizes of face frame finish stock.

TABLE XXXIX

FACE FRAME LUMBER FOOTAGE CONSTANTS

Size of Stock	Constant	Size of Stock	Constant
1" x 2"	.166	1¼" x 2"	.208
1" x 3"	.25	1¼" x 3"	.312
1" x 4"	.33	1¼" x 4"	.416
1" x 5"	.416	1¼" x 5"	.52
1" x 6"	.50	1¼" x 6"	.624
1¼" x 1¼"	.13	1¼" x 8"	.832

To use the table proceed as follows:

1. Figure the linear feet of face frame material required, listing by thickness and width.

2. Select constant which represents the correct size of the face frame material.

3. Multiply total linear feet of face frame stock by this constant. Result equals board feet of lumber. Convert to the next whole foot.

4. Continue for the various sizes of face frame material.

5. Combine the various results. The answer is the total number of board feet of lumber in the face frame (or frames).

ESTIMATOR'S CHECKING LIST

An estimator's checking list is very essential when "taking-off" various items required to construct a building. The following table has been developed as an aid to estimating and is in six parts, as follows: *foundation, framing, exterior finish, interior finish, miscellaneous and hardware,* and *special items.* The various parts of the list are based on the preceding short cut material tables, XXXVI–XXXVIII, inclusive, page 177 to 219.

A check-up measurement sheet as shown on page 5 is invaluable to use in conjunction with the list below.

To use the list proceed as follows:

1. Start at the top of each division of the table and check each item as to need. The following questions should be asked:

   a. Is there a need for this item? This is determined by checking the plans and specifications.

   b. What are the dimensions of this item or unit of work?

   c. What do the specifications say about the quality of material; the proportion of mix (if one is specified), etc.?

2. How much material is needed in terms of pieces, linear feet, square feet, etc.? It is on this point that the actual estimating work begins. The measurement check-up sheet should be consulted as most of the linear feet and area measurements are already estimated on this sheet. Use the short cut rules whenever possible, listing by large units of worth rather than by individual items.

ESTIMATOR'S CHECKING LIST
TABLE XL

I. FOUNDATION

1. *Special job office*

2. *Laying out*

3. *Grading*

4. *Excavating*
    Trenches
    Basement
    Porch fills
    Back fills

5. *Concrete*
    Walls and footings
        Exterior
        Dwarf
        Basement
        Retaining
    Piers
    Fireplaces
    Entrances
    Flat work
        Driveway approach
        Porches
        Garage floors
        Driveway
        Entrance platforms
        Rear platforms
        Walks
        Rough concrete
            under brick paving
    Steps
        Front
        Rear
        Basement

6. *Steel*
    Reinforcing in footings
            in walls
            in porch
                floors

7. *Brickwork*
        Porch floors
        Porch edges
        Walks
        Steps

II. FRAMING

1. *Underpinning*
        Mudsill
        Pier blocks
        Cribbing
        Girders
        Posts
        Braces

2. *Floors*
        # squares
        Double joists
        Headers under partitions
        Vent headers
        Headers over girders
        Fireplace framing
        Bridging

3. *Walls*
        # squares
        Top headers
        Diagonal boarding

4. *Ceiling*
        # squares

5. *Roof*
   # squares
   Bracing
   Gable studs

6. *Stairs, rough framing*

7. *Extra for treated lumber*

8. *Special beam work*

9. *Scaffolding*

10. *Base grounds*

III. EXTERIOR FINISH

1. *Roofing*
   # squares
   Ridges and hips

2. *Frames*
   Door
   Window
   Gable
   Garage
   Gas Meter

3. *Cornice*
   Horizontal
   Gables

4. *Porch*
   Columns
   Ceilings

5. *Siding*
   Paper
   Cornice boards
   Water table

6. *Special work on bay or dormer windows*

7. *Balconies*

8. *Special flashing*

9. *Special mill work*

10. *Front entrance*

11. *Scaffolding*

12. *Pergolas*

IV. INTERIOR FINISH

1. *Door, windows, screws and shutters*
   Doors
     Exterior
     Interior
     Garage
     Gas meter
   Windows
     Windows or sash
     Transoms
   Screens
     Interior
     Exterior
   Shutters

2. *Trim*
   Doors
     Exterior
     Interior
     Sliding
     Cased openings
     Garage
   Windows
   Base and shoe
   Shoe corners
   Picture mouldings
   Cornice mouldings
   Wainscot cap
   Drapery boxes
   Closet shelving, poles
     and hookstrips
   Threshold

Cedar lining
   Mill sets (special set-
     ups at mill)
   3 ply under linoleum

3. *Paneled walls and ceilings*

4. *Cabinets*

   Kitchen, porch, bath,
     living room, hall
   3 ply

5. *Drawers and bread boards*

6. *C. C. Doors*

7. *Stairs*

8. *Hardwood floors*

V. HARDWARE AND MISCELLANEOUS

1. *Hardware*

   Rough
     Bolts and nails
   Finish
     Surface and hanging
     hardware for all
     windows, doors,
     cabinets
   Sash balances

2. *Miscellaneous*

   Incidentals
     Permits and fees
     Sales tax
     Cartage

Water and power
   Water meter
   Fuel bill (power saw)
   Power bill
   Water bill
Telephone
Building and insula-
   tion paper
Built-in accessories
   Door grilles
   Iron receptacle
   Mail box
   Medicine cabinet
   Milk bottle holders
   Shoe racks
   Vents

VI. SPECIAL ITEMS

1. *Architect's fees* *

2. *Extra labor costs*

   Watchman
   Bonuses

3. *Exterior items*

   Waterproofing
   Insulation
   Staff Work
   Overhead garage doors
   Awnings
   Skylights
   Landscaping
   Sprinkler system
   Fence

*An architect's fees for drawing up plans and specifications are usually based on a percentage of the total building costs. An additional fee is charged if he also superintends the construction. This item is listed above as sometimes an architect will work with a contractor on a building project and the contractor will include in his bid the costs of the plans and specifications.

4. *Interior items*

    Linoleum
    Shades and blinds
    Drapery track
    Mantel
    Mirrors
    Wall paper
    Elevator
    Refrigerator
    Wall safe
    Wall beds

5. *Repairing*

    List items as called for
      on plans

6. *Wrecking*

    Tearing down
    Cleaning
    Hauling
    Salvage

CHAPTER IX

LABOR HOURS PER UNIT OF WORK

THERE ARE MANY variations possible in the amount of work a carpenter can do in a given period of time. One man may work faster than another because of *greater skill* or *longer trade experience*.

The *kind* of work done also affects the amount produced. A cheap job can naturally be done at lower cost than a job on which the contractor demands only the best work.

Another factor which affects the time required by a carpenter to do a job is that of the *construction methods* to be followed. Building ordinances vary in many items when one city is compared with another, and architects specify different types of construction.

A fourth factor which makes it hard to state the amount of carpenter work which can be done in a given period of time is the difficulty involved because of *using the same term to describe two widely differing jobs*. To illustrate: A stock question usually asked a newcomer on the job is: "How many doors can you hang in one day?" Yet doors differ in thickness, size, shape, weight, and kind of lumber. Naturally a circle top door cannot be hung in the same length of time as a square top door; neither can a hardwood door be hung as quickly as a soft pine door. Baseboard put on *before* the job is plastered takes much less time than putting it on after the plastering is done. There is, then, no standard of comparison unless the details of the different jobs are approximately the same.

226

Weather conditions have much to do with the speed of a skilled craftsman, and must be considered when making up a labor estimate. Extremely hot or cold weather will slow up any carpenter.

One other important item which makes a difference in the daily accomplishments of a carpenter must be mentioned. *Power hand tools* are being used quite extensively in many parts of our country; the addition of a power saw to the carpenter's equipment has increased his production greatly. These tools are usually furnished by the contractor.

The many possible situations enumerated above make it difficult to formulate rules which can be used to make accurate estimates of carpentry work. The problem is simplified, somewhat, if the *average amount of work* is used as a basis for the carpenter labor estimate. By average is meant the amount of work which one man can do under normal conditions. Neither a slow or a fast man is considered, but about half way between these two extremes (a contractor will never have all slow or all fast men).

The results obtained by using the following rules are in hours. *Rate per hour times number of hours equals estimated cost of carpenter labor.* The rules are based on hand tool production for two reasons: (1) All contractors do not have or use power hand tools. (2) A contractor must get a return on his investment; if hand tool labor is figured, the amount saved by using a power tool offsets the overhead costs of owning and operating it.

Judgment and accurate record keeping will determine the accuracy of the results obtained by using table XLI, page 228.

The rules are divided into three major divisions, namely: framing, exterior finish, and interior finish.

The constants were developed by figuring the carpenter's rate of pay as $1.00 per hour.

After the labor hours have been determined for a unit of work, check the result with the job to be done and allow for any special construction problem which may require additional time. This additional time should be added to the result found by using the rules.

TABLE XLI

LABOR HOURS PER UNIT OF WORK

I. FRAMING

Building Parts	Rule
Mudsill:	Linear feet x .06 equals hours.
Girders:	Set 50-70 linear feet per hour.
Posts:	Set 4-6 posts per hour.
Joists:	Floor area x .015 equals hours.
Sub-floor:	Floor area x .015 or .02 equals hours.
Walls and Partitions:	Wall area x .04 equals hours.
Ceiling:	Area x .01 equals hours.
Gable roof:	Floor area x .025 or .03 equals hours.
Hip roof:	Floor area x .04 or .045 equals hours.

II. EXTERIOR FINISH

Building Parts	Rule
Window and door frames:	To make one window or door frame allow 1 hour.
	To set one window or door frame allow ½ hour.
	To make and set one garage door frame allow 1 hour.

II. Exteriot Finish—*Continued*

Cornice:	
1 member mould	Linear feet x .06 equals hours.
2 member mould	Linear feet x .09 equals hours.
3 member mould	Linear feet x .12 equals hours.
4 member mould	Linear feet x .15 equals hours.
	Note:
	The term two (three or four) member cornice mould means a mould consisting of two separate parts assembled to make a complete cornice.
	The same rules can be applied to a belt course or water table.
Siding:	Square feet of siding x .06 equals hours.
	Note:
	This will vary greatly on account of the thickness and width of the stock and the kind of joints required at the corners and windows and door casings.
Corner Boards:	Number of corners x .5 equals hours.

III. Interior Finish

Building Parts	Rule
Baseboard:	
Before plastering:	Linear feet x .04 equals hours.
After plastering:	Linear feet x .07 equals hours.
Base shoe:	Linear feet x .025 equals hours.

III. Interior Finish—*Continued*

Building Parts	Rule
Drawers:	To make an average drawer allow 1 hour.
C. C. Doors	To fit and hang a 5 ply C. C. door allow 1 hour.
	To fit and hang a paneled C. C. door allow ½ hour.
Drapery boxes:	To make and install one box allow 1 hour.
Windows and sash:	To fit double hung sash and put on all trim and hardware allow 2¼ hours. If sash balances are used add ¼ hour. If no interior casings are required deduct ½ hour.
	To fit and hang one casement sash to swing *in,* and put on all trim and hardware, allow 1¾ hours. If no interior casings are used deduct ½ hour.
	To fit *one pair* casement sash to swing *in* and put on all trim and hardware, allow 2¾ hours. If no interior casing deduct ½ hour.
	To fit and hang one casement sash to swing *out,* trim the interior of the frame, hang the screen and put on all hardware, allow 2½ hours.

III. Interior Finish—*Continued*

Building Parts	Rule

Picture moulding:
Cornice moulding:
  One member mould:
  Two member mould:
	Allow 2 hours per room.
	
	Allow 4 hours per room.
	Allow 6 hours per room.

Doors:	To make, set and case a door jamb, fit and hang door and apply stops and hardware, allow 4 hours. If no interior casings are used deduct 1 hour.
	To make, set and case door jamb, fit and hang *one pair* of inside doors, apply stops and hardware, allow 5¼ hours. If no interior casings are used deduct 1 hour.
	To case front door frame, fit and hang door and apply hardware, allow 4 hours. If no interior casings are used deduct ½ hour. If front screen door is used add 1¼ hours.
	To case French door frame, fit and hang *one pair* of French doors, fit and apply stops and hardware, allow 4 hours. If two screen doors are used, add 2 hours.
	To make, set and case jambs for a cased opening allow 2 hours.

III. Interior Finish—*Continued*

Building Parts	Rule (No cabinet door or drawer labor included)*
Kitchen sink: See Fig. 78, page 204	To glue up material for and construct sink cabinet with face frame *ready to receive* doors, drawers and tile allow 1 hour per linear foot of cabinet. Note: For cabinet 6′ or less allow 1½ hours per linear foot.
Dish cabinet: See Fig. 79, page 205	To construct an average size dish cabinet with face frame *ready to receive* doors allow 3 hours.
Kitchen cabinet and cooler: See Fig. 80, page 206	To glue material for and construct combination cabinet with face frame *ready to receive* doors, drawers and cooler shelves allow 16 hours for 6′ width and 18 hours for 8′ width.
Dish and drawer cabinet: See Fig. 81, page 208	To glue material for and construct cabinet with face frame *ready to receive* doors and drawers allow 12 hours for 3′ or 4′ width.
Broom cupboard: See Fig. 82 page 210	To construct cupboard with face frame *ready to receive* door, if no gluing allow 4 hours, if jamb and shelf are glued allow 5 hours.

*Door hanging and drawer making can easily be figured as separate items as they lend themselves to a somewhat standardized unit-of-labor cost. See page 230.

III. Interior Finish—*Continued*

Building Parts	Rule (No cabinet door or drawer labor included)*
Linen cabinet: See Fig. 83, page 212	To glue material for and construct cabinet with face frame *ready to receive* doors and drawers allow 10 hours. Note: This assumes regular door jamb (into which cabinet is constructed) is already set and cased.
Medicine cabinet: See Fig. 84, page 214	To construct on the bench *ready to receive* door; set and fasten into opening allow 3 hours. Note: If a metal cabinet, complete with mirror door, is purchased then labor only needs to cover installation. This will vary with the size of the cabinet and the construction conditions to be met.
Bookcase: See Fig. 85, page 216	To construct bookcase with jamb bored for adjustable shelf brackets and with face frame *ready to receive* doors, (if any are required) allow 6 hours for 3′ or 4′ width.
Mantel shelf: See Fig. 86, page 218	To glue material for and construct mantel shelf complete with moulding allow 8 to 12 hours depending on number of mouldings and difficulty of job.

*See footnote, page 232.

CHAPTER X

CARPENTRY MENSURATION

THERE ARE CERTAIN mensuration rules used by all persons who have to "take-off" a bill of material for a building. The preceding chapters have assumed that the estimator is familiar with these rules. As an aid, however, to the carpenter apprentice who has yet to learn basic estimating procedures, the following material has been developed.

The mensuration rules are divided into three parts as follows:

1. *Linear measurement rules* are applied to perimeters of squares and rectangles and the hypotenuse of a right angle triangle.

2. *Area measurement* rules as applied to floors, ceilings, walls, gables and roofs.

3. *Volume measurement* rules as applied to excavating and concrete.

PERIMETER RULES*

The perimeter is the distance around a square or rectangle. The need for finding this measurement constantly arises in the estimator's work. The following rules indicate how to find perimeters for different shaped buildings.

*See page 159.

1. *Square Building*:
   To find the perimeter of a square build-ing, multiply the length of one side by 4. Fractional building measurements are in-creased to next half or whole foot, before computing.

Fig. 88

2. *Rectangular Building*:
   To find the perimeter of a rectangular building, add the width and length to-gether and multiply by 2. Fractional building measurements are increased to next half or whole foot before com-puting.

Fig. 89

3. *Circular Building*:
   To find the circumference of a circular building multiply the diameter by "pi" (3.1416). In most cases $3\frac{1}{7}$ is sufficiently accurate for the value of "pi". Fractional building diameter is increased to next half or whole foot before computing.

Fig. 90

4. *Building with Corner Off-set*:
   To find the perimeter of a building with a cor-ner off-set the rule for a square or rectangular building may be ap-plied. This is true be-cause x equals y, and r equals s. The perimeter is the same even though one or more corners of the building may have been removed.

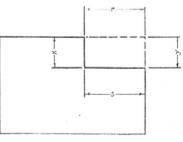

Fig. 91

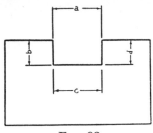

FIG. 92

5. *Building with Wall Off-set*:

To find the perimeter of a building with a wall off-set use the rule for a square or rectangular building and add the length of the offset walls as indicated by b and d.   a and c are equal.

HYPOTHENUSE LENGTHS

The carpentry situations that require the finding of a hypotenuse are four: namely herring-bone bridging, braces, rafters and stair horses or stair stringers.

The steel square can be used to find the hypotenuse. Let one number on the tongue of the square represent the rise; another number on the blade of the square represent the run; then measure diagonally from one number to the other, using an ordinary rule, or preferably another steel square. The result will be inches and part of an inch, which are called feet and inches, respectively.

1. *Herring-bone Bridging*: To find the length of stock to make one piece of herring-bone bridging, use the following rule. The width of the joist equals the rise of the bridging; the spacing be-

FIG. 93

tween joists equals the run of the bridging. Let the steel square represent the rise and run and measure the diagonal.

2. *Brace Length*: To find the length of the stock to make a brace use one of the following rules. The rise of the brace is the height of the wall; the run of the brace is the horizontal distance along the plate line. For

Fig. 94

estimating purposes the run measurement is always equal to the rise. See figure 12, page 35.

(a) Let the steel square represent the rise and run and measure the diagonal.

(b) Multiply the wall height by the constant 1.414.

3. *Common Rafter, Shed Roof*: To find the length of stock for a common rafter, use one of the following rules. The difference in height of the two walls that support the rafter is the rise of the rafter; the width of the building is the run of the rafter.

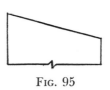

Fig. 95

(a) Multiply the run of the rafter by a constant which corresponds to a given pitch. See table XI on page 61.

(b) Let the steel square represent the rise and run and measure the diagonal.

(c) Scale the length on the elevation sheet of the blueprint.

NOTE: These rules give length from ridge to plate line only. If there is a cornice overhang, it must be added to get total length of rafter stock.

4. *Common Rafter, Gable Roof*: To find the length of stock for a common rafter, use one of the following rules. The height of the ridge above the top plate line, is the rise of the rafter; one-half the span of the roof is the run of the rafter. Span is total width of the building.

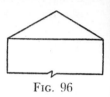

FIG. 96

(a) Multiply the run of the rafter by a constant which corresponds to a given pitch. See table XI an page 61.

(b) Let the steel square represent the rise and run, measure the diagonal.

(c) Scale the length on the elevation sheet of the blueprint.

5. *Hip Rafter*: To find the length of stock for a hip rafter, use one of the following rules. The rise of the common rafter is the rise of the hip rafter; the *diagonal* of a square

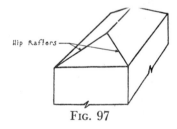

FIG. 97

whose measurements are one-half the span is the run of the rafter.

(a) Multiply the span of the roof by a constant which corresponds to the given pitch. See table XII on page 65.

(b) Let the steel square represent rise and run and measure diagonal.

6. *Stair Horse*:
To find length
of a stair horse,
use the follow-
ing rules. The
vertical distance
from finished
floor to finished
floor above is the
rise; the hori-
zontal distance is

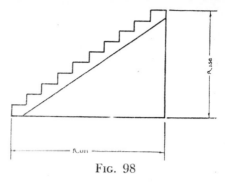

FIG. 98

found by multiplying tread run by the number of
treads.

(a) Let the steel square represent rise and run and
measure diagonal.

(b) Scale the length on the detail sheet of the blueprint.

AREA RULES

The *area* problems that the estimator meets can be
classified into four types: squares, rectangles, triangles,
and circles. Building parts are partitions, walls, floors,
ceilings, roofs and gables. Rules for finding the area of
these parts of a building follow:

1. *Partitions*: The area of a
partition is found by multiplying the length by the
height. Fractional building
measurements are increased
to the next half or whole
foot before computing.

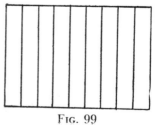

FIG. 99

2. *Walls*:

(a) *Straight*: To find the area of a straight wall, multiply the length by the height. Fractional building measurements are increased to next half or whole foot, before computing.

(b) *Building*: To find the area of the walls of a building multiply the perimeter by the height. Fractional building measurements are increased to next half or whole foot, before computing. The perimeter is really the same as if the walls were stretched out as illustrated. The height of

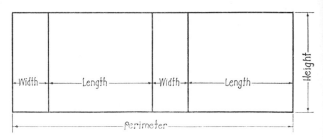

Fig. 100

an outside wall may include the framed wall only; the framed wall plus the thickness of the mudsill and the width of the floor joists; or, it may be taken from the ground to top of the fire wall, depending on the intended use of the figures that represent the area.

(c) *Room*: To find the area of the walls of a room, multiply the perimeter by the height. Divide answer by 9, if square yards are desired. Fractional building measurements are increased to next half or whole foot, before computing.

(d) *Firewall*: To find area of the inside face of a firewall, multiply building perimeter by height of wall at the *lowest* point of the roof. Fractional building measurements are increased to next half or whole foot, before computing.

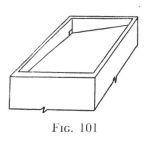

Fig. 101

3. *Floors*:

(a) *Square Building*: To find the floor area of a square building, mutiply the length of one side by itself. Fractional building measurements are increased to next half or whole foot, before computing.

Fig. 102

(b) *Rectangular Building*: To find the area of a rectangular shaped building, multiply the width by the length. Fractional building measurements are increased to next half or whole foot, before computing.

Fig. 103

(c) *Circular Building*: To find the area of a circular building, multiply the radius^2 × pi (3.1416). Expressed in another way: mutiply diameter^2 × .7584. A fractional diameter is increased to next half or whole foot, before computing.

Fig. 104

(d) *Building with Take-Away Areas*: To find the area of buildings shaped as shown in sketch the rule is: Multiply the largest width measurement by the largest length measurement and subtract the "take-away" areas. Fractional building

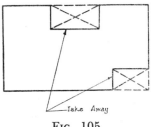

measurements are increased to next half or whole foot, before computing.

The same rule may be applied when it is desired to find the floor area of only part of the house.

FIG. 105

(1) Figure the total floor area; (2) Figure area of room or rooms that are not to be included; (3) Deduct rooms areas from total floor area.

NOTE: When figuring floor areas to determine the amount of hardwood floor, inside measurements, as scaled or "read" on the floor plan, are used. Increase inch measurements to $\frac{1}{4}$, $\frac{1}{2}$ or $\frac{3}{4}$ of a foot.

4. *Ceiling*: This problem is a duplicate of the floor situation, hence the rules, as given for floor areas, may be applied.

5. *Roofs.**

The mensuration rules for figuring roof areas are divided into two parts; namely, equal pitch roofs and unequal pitch roofs.

*See Simplified Roof Framing, Wilson & Werner. (McGraw-Hill Book Co.) for detailed information on roof framing.

EQUAL PITCH ROOF AREA

The roof area problems are based on the type of roof. Roof area increases if there is a cornice. The length of rafter that overhangs the building must be added to the rafter length from ridge to plate line. The roof projection over the gable ends must be added to the building length measurement. See figure 51, page 94.

(a) *Flat Roof:* The area of a flat roof is determined the same as the area of a floor. Therefore, see *Floors,* page 241.

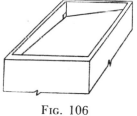

Fig. 106

(b) *Shed Roof:* The area of a shed roof is found by multiplying the rafter length by the ridge length. Fractional building measurements are increased to half or whole feet before computing.

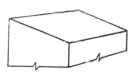

Fig. 107

(c) *Gable Roof:* The area of a gable roof is found by multiplying the rafter length by the ridge length and then multiplying this result by 2. Fractional building measurements are increased to next half or whole foot, before computing.

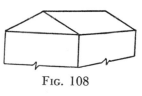

Fig. 108

(d) *Gambrel Roof:* The area of a gambrel roof is computed the same as a gable and shed roof. For both the steep and flat parts of the roof, rafter length × 2 equals area. Combine results.

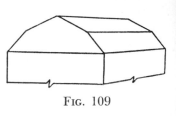

FIG. 109

(e) *Hip Roofs:* It is not difficult to find the area of a hip roof, as it is figured the same as a gable roof. The hip roof is made up of four parts shaped as shown in figure 111. These part can be fitted

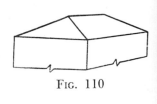

FIG. 110

together in the form of a parallelogram, which in turn can be changed into a rectangle. The area of

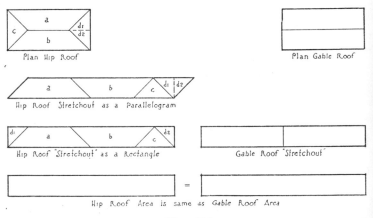

Plan Hip Roof

Plan Gable Roof

Hip Roof Stretchout as a Parallelogram

Hip Roof "Stretchout" as a Rectangle

Gable Roof "Stretchout"

Hip Roof Area is same as Gable Roof Area

FIG. 111

this rectangle is the same as the two rectangles that form a gable roof. The rule, therefore, for a hip roof area is, eave length × common rafter length × 2. Eave length equals building length plus cornice run at each end. All fractional building measurements are increased to next half or whole foot before computing.

NOTE: Short-cut method:

A short-cut method of finding the roof area of an equal pitch hip roof can be used. The rule is: floor area multiplied by constant based on roof pitch increase equals roof area. See table of constants page 61. If the building has a cornice, the plan area of the roof must be estimated. To find plan area, add the horizontal roof projection measurements to the floor plan measurements, then multiply the width × the length.

(f) *Intersecting Roof*: Figure the floor area. Multiply this result by the correct roof area constant selected from the table on page 61. The result equals the area of an intersecting roof. All

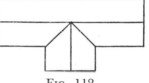

FIG. 112

fractional building measurements are increased to next half or whole foot before computing.

UNEQUAL PITCH ROOF AREA

(a) *Gable Roof, Plates Same Height*: This roof is easily figured as two separate shed roofs.

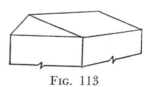

FIG. 113

(b) *Gable Roof, Plates Not Same Height*: This roof is easily figured as two separate shed roofs.

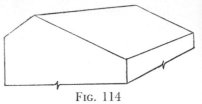

FIG. 114

(c) *Intersecting Roof*: For an intersecting roof with two different pitches, figure the actual floor area below each part of the roof. Then multiply each area by the correct constant selected

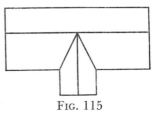

FIG. 115

from the table on page 61. Two roof pitches require two different constants.

NOTE: To find the floor area:

(1) Find the total floor area of the main part of the building.

(2) Then deduct the triangular shaped "take-away" area. Result is net floor area below the main roof.

(3) For wing, find the area of the square or rectangular part. Add the "take-away" area found above. Result is net floor area below the roof of the wing. Fractional building measurements are increased to next half or whole foot, before computing.

6. *Gable Areas*: A gable area is the triangular shaped piece of wall formed by the slope of the rafter. Gable area rules are classified into two parts, equal pitch

roofs and unequal pitch roofs. To find this area several rules are needed based on the type of roof.

GABLE AREAS FOR EQUAL PITCH ROOFS

(a) *Shed Roof*: Multiply the width of the building by the height of the roof and divide result by 2. Fractional building measurements are increased to next half or whole foot, before computing.

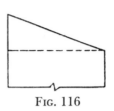

FIG. 116

(b) *Gable Roof*: Mutiply the span of the rafters by the height of the roof and divide result by 2. Fractional building measurements are increased to next half or whole foot, before computing.

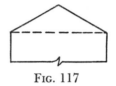

FIG. 117

(c) *Combination Shed and Gable Roof*: The gable areas are figured as follows:

FIG. 118

1. Figure the shed and gable roofs as previously explained.

2. Add these results.

(d) *Gambrel Roof*: There are four parts to this gable: the area of the flat gable; the area of the two shed roof gables; and the rectangular part. To find the total area:

1. The gable for the flat part of the roof is the same as a regular gable.

2. The gable area of the steep part of the roof is the same as a shed roof.

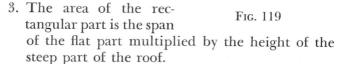

FIG. 119

3. The area of the rectangular part is the span of the flat part multiplied by the height of the steep part of the roof.

4. Add these results.

GABLE AREAS FOR UNEQUAL PITCH ROOFS

(a) *Gable Roof, Plate Same Height*: If the plate line of the building is the same height and the roof has two slants, as illustrated, multiply the span by the

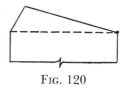

FIG. 120

roof height and divide the result by two. Fractional measurements are increased to next half or whole foot, before computing.

(b) *Gable Roof, Plate Not Same Height*: The gable areas for this type roof are figured as outlined below. All fractional building measurements are increased to next half or whole foot, before computing.

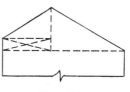

FIG. 121

1. Multiply the rafter run by the rafter rise of the larger part of the roof and divide by two.

2. Repeat this process for the smaller part.

3. Find the area of the rectangle. This is rafter run of short rafter multiplied by the difference in plate height.

4. Add these results.

VOLUME RULES

The carpentry situations in estimating that require a mathematical solution to find volume are excavating and concrete forms.

1. *Excavating*:

   (a) *Trenches*: To find the cubic feet or cubic yards of earth in a trench, each measurement must be of the same mathematical value (width and depth are usually given in inches). Therefore, the rule is: width multiplied by depth multiplied by length (all dimensions in feet). If cubic yards are desired, divide the results by 27. Increase fractional length measurements to next half or whole foot, before computing.

   (b) *Basement*: The measurements for a basement are usually expressed in feet. Therefore, the rule is: width multiplied by length multiplied by depth. If cubic yards are desired, divide result by 27. Use all measurements as given on the blueprint.

2. *Concrete Forms*:*

(a) *Footings*: To figure the content of a form for a concrete footing, multiply width by depth by length. Each measurement must be the same mathematical denomination.

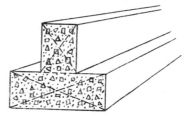

Fig. 122

Fractional length measurements are increased to next half or whole foot, before computing. Use depth and width measurements, as given on the blueprint.

(b) *Foundation Walls*: To find the volume of a form for a concrete foundation wall, multiply width by the height by the length. Each measurement must be of the same mathematical denomination.

Fractional length measurements are increased to next half or whole foot, before computing. Use width and height measurements, as given on the blueprint.

(c) *Basement Walls*: See figure 123. To find the volume of a form for a concrete basement wall, multiply the wall thickness by the outside perimeter by the height. Use *outside* width, length and height measurements as given on the blue-

*See Table XXVIII, page 160.

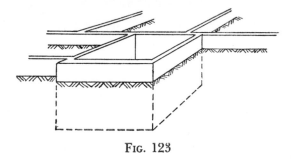

Fig. 123

print. Each measurement must be of the same mathematical denomination.

CHAPTER XI

MATHEMATICAL REFERENCE TABLES

SOME OF THE more commonly used mathematical tables are included in the following pages to provide the estimator with readily accessible information.

TABLE XLII
PARTS-OF-A-FOOT CONVERSION TABLE

	0″	1/8″	1/4″	3/8″	1/2″	5/8″	3/4″	7/8″
0″	.000	.010	.021	.031	.042	.052	.063	.073
1″	.083	.094	.104	.115	.125	.135	.146	.156
2″	.167	.177	.188	.198	.208	.219	.229	.240
3″	.250	.260	.271	.281	.292	.302	.313	.323
4″	.333	.344	.354	.365	.375	.385	.396	.406
5″	.417	.427	.438	.448	.458	.469	.479	.490
6″	.500	.510	.521	.531	.542	.552	.563	.573
7″	.583	.594	.604	.615	.625	.635	.646	.656
8″	.667	.677	.688	.698	.708	.719	.729	.740
9″	.750	.760	.771	.781	.792	.802	.813	.823
10″	.833	.844	.854	.865	.875	.885	.896	.906
11″	.917	.927	.938	.948	.958	.969	.979	.990

To use the table proceed as follows:

1. Locate the number of whole inches in the left hand column.
2. Follow this line across until directly below the number of parts of an inch.
3. Read at this location the decimal part of a foot.

DECIMAL EQUIVALENT TABLE

The following table has been included to provide a quick method of converting a decimal to a fraction.

TABLE XLIII
DECIMAL EQUIVALENT TABLE

Decimal	Fractional Equivalent	Decimal	Fractional Equivalent
.01562	$\frac{1}{64}$	.51562	$\frac{33}{64}$
.03125	$\frac{1}{32}$	.53125	$\frac{17}{32}$
.04687	$\frac{3}{64}$	.54687	$\frac{35}{64}$
.0625	$\frac{1}{16}$	.5625	$\frac{9}{16}$
.07812	$\frac{5}{64}$	.57812	$\frac{37}{64}$
.09375	$\frac{3}{32}$	.59375	$\frac{19}{32}$
.10937	$\frac{7}{64}$	.60937	$\frac{39}{64}$
.1250	$\frac{1}{8}$	.6250	$\frac{5}{8}$
.14062	$\frac{9}{64}$	.64062	$\frac{41}{64}$
.15625	$\frac{5}{32}$	.65625	$\frac{21}{32}$
.17187	$\frac{11}{64}$	.67187	$\frac{43}{64}$
.1875	$\frac{3}{16}$	.6875	$\frac{11}{16}$
.20312	$\frac{13}{64}$	.70312	$\frac{45}{64}$
.21875	$\frac{7}{32}$	.71875	$\frac{23}{32}$
.23437	$\frac{15}{64}$	.73437	$\frac{47}{64}$
.2500	$\frac{1}{4}$	.7500	$\frac{3}{4}$
.26562	$\frac{17}{64}$	.76562	$\frac{49}{64}$
.28125	$\frac{9}{32}$	.78125	$\frac{25}{32}$
.29687	$\frac{19}{64}$	.79687	$\frac{51}{64}$
.3125	$\frac{5}{16}$	.8125	$\frac{13}{10}$
.32812	$\frac{21}{64}$	.82812	$\frac{53}{64}$
.34375	$\frac{11}{32}$	.84375	$\frac{27}{32}$
.35937	$\frac{23}{64}$	.85937	$\frac{55}{64}$
.3750	$\frac{3}{8}$	.8750	$\frac{7}{8}$
.39062	$\frac{25}{64}$	.89062	$\frac{57}{64}$
.40625	$\frac{13}{32}$	.90625	$\frac{29}{32}$
.42187	$\frac{27}{64}$	.92187	$\frac{59}{64}$
.4375	$\frac{7}{16}$	.9375	$\frac{15}{16}$
.45312	$\frac{29}{64}$	.95312	$\frac{61}{64}$
.46875	$\frac{15}{32}$	.96875	$\frac{31}{32}$
.48437	$\frac{31}{64}$	.98437	$\frac{63}{64}$
.5000	$\frac{1}{2}$	1.00000	1

To use the table:

1. Locate the decimal to be changed to a fraction.
2. Read the fractional equivalent.

LUMBER RECKONER

As an aid to the carpenter estimator when converting pieces of lumber to board feet the following table has been included:

TABLE XLIV

LUMBER RECKONER

Table shows number of board feet in one piece

Sizes, in.	Length, ft.										
	10	12	14	16	18	20	22	24	26	28	30
1 × 2	1⅔	2	2⅓	2⅔	3	3⅓					
1 × 3	2½	3	3½	4	4½	5					
1 × 4	3⅓	4	4⅔	5⅓	6	6⅔					
1 × 6	5	6	7	8	9	10					
1 × 8	6⅔	8	9⅓	10⅓	12	13⅓					
1 × 10	8⅓	10	11⅔	13⅓	15	16⅔					
1 × 12	10	12	14	16	18	20					
1 × 14	11⅔	14	16⅓	18⅔	22⅔	23⅓					
1 × 16	13⅓	16	18⅔	21⅓	24	26⅔					
1¼ × 4	4⅙	5	5⅚	6⅔							
1¼ × 6	6⅓	7½	8⅓	10							
1¼ × 8	8⅓	10	11⅔	13⅓							
1¼ × 10	10 5/12	12½	14 7/12	16⅔							
1¼ × 12	12½	15	17½	20							
1½ × 4	5	6	7	8							
1½ × 6	7½	9	10½	12							
1½ × 8	10	12	14	16							
1½ × 10	12½	15	17½	20							
1½ × 12	15	18	21	24							
2 × 4	6⅔	8	9⅓	10⅔	12	13⅓	14⅔	16	17⅓	18⅔	20
2 × 6	10	12	14	16	18	20	22	24	26	28	30
2 × 8	13⅓	16	18⅔	21⅓	24	26⅔	29⅓	32	34⅔	37⅓	40
2 × 10	16⅔	20	23⅓	26⅔	30	33⅓	36⅔	40	43⅓	46⅔	50
2 × 12	20	24	28	32	36	40	44	48	52	56	60
2 × 14	23⅓	28	32⅔	37⅓	42	46⅔	51⅓	56	60⅔	65⅓	70
2 × 16	26⅔	32	37⅓	42⅔	48	53⅓	58⅔	64	69⅓	74⅔	80
2½ × 12	25	30	35	40	45	50	55	60	65	70	75
2½ × 14	29⅙	35	40⅚	46⅔	52½	58⅓	64⅙	70	75⅚	81⅔	87½
2½ × 16	33⅓	40	46⅔	53⅓	60	66⅔	73⅓	80	86⅔	93⅓	100

LUMBER RECKONER (Continued)

Table shows number of board feet in one piece

Sizes, in.		Length, ft.										
		10	12	14	16	18	20	22	24	26	28	30
3	× 6	15	18	21	24	27	30	33	36	39	42	45
3	× 8	20	24	28	32	36	40	44	48	52	56	60
3	×10	25	30	35	40	45	50	55	60	65	70	75
3	×12	30	36	42	48	54	60	66	72	78	84	90
3	×14	35	42	49	56	63	70	77	84	91	98	105
3	×16	40	48	56	64	72	80	88	96	104	112	120
4	× 4	13⅓	16	18⅔	21⅓	24	26⅔	29⅓	32	34⅔	37⅓	40
4	× 6	20	24	28	32	36	40	44	46	52	56	60
4	× 8	26⅔	32	37⅓	42⅔	48	53⅓	58⅔	64	69⅓	74⅔	80
4	×10	33⅓	40	46⅔	53⅓	60	66⅔	73⅓	80	86⅔	93⅓	100
4	×12	40	48	56	64	72	80	88	96	104	112	120
4	×14	46⅔	56	65⅓	74⅔	84	93⅓	102⅔	112	121⅓	130⅔	140
6	× 6	30	36	42	48	54	60	66	72	78	84	90
6	× 8	40	48	56	64	72	80	88	96	104	112	120
6	×10	50	60	70	80	90	100	110	120	130	140	150
6	×12	60	72	84	96	108	120	132	144	156	168	180
6	×14	70	84	98	112	126	140	154	168	182	196	210
6	×16	80	96	112	128	144	160	176	192	208	224	240
8	× 8	53⅓	64	74⅔	85⅓	96	106⅔	117⅓	128	138⅔	149⅓	160
8	×10	66⅔	80	93⅓	106⅔	120	133⅓	146⅔	160	173⅓	186⅔	200
8	×12	80	96	112	128	144	160	176	192	208	224	240
8	×14	93⅓	112	130⅔	149⅓	168	186⅔	205⅓	224	242⅔	261⅓	280
10	×10	83⅓	100	116⅔	133⅓	150	166⅔	183⅓	200	216⅔	233⅓	250
10	×12	100	120	140	160	180	200	220	240	260	280	300
10	×14	116⅔	140	163⅓	186⅔	210	233⅓	256⅔	280	303⅓	326⅔	350
10	×16	133⅓	160	186⅔	213⅓	240	266⅔	293⅓	320	346⅔	373⅓	400
12	×12	120	144	168	192	216	240	264	288	312	336	360
12	×14	140	168	196	224	252	280	308	336	364	392	420
12	×16	160	192	224	256	288	320	352	384	416	448	480
14	×14	163⅓	196	228⅔	261⅓	294	326⅔	359⅓	392	424⅔	457⅓	490
14	×16	186⅔	224	261⅓	298⅔	336	373⅓	410⅔	448	485⅓	522⅔	560

To use the table proceed as follows:

1. Determine quantity and dimensions of lumber required.

2. Select these sizes in the table and read the number of board feet in *one* piece.

3. Multiply constant selected by the number of pieces required.

TABLE XLV

MENSURATION

1. Square
   Perimeter   = 4 × side
   Area   = side squared
   Diagonal   = 1.414 × side

2. Rectangle
   Perimeter   = 2 × length + 2 × width
   Area   = length × width
   Diagonal   = square root of the sum of the length squared plus the width squared

3. Prallelogram
   Perimeter   = sum of 4 sides
   Area   = base × height

4. Trapezoid
   Perimeter   = sum of 4 sides
   Area   = sum of 2 bases divided by 2 and multiplied by height

5. Triangle
   Perimeter   = sum of 3 sides
   Area   = base × ½ altitude

6. Hexagon
   Perimeter   = sum of 6 sides or 6 × one side
   Area   = side × 3 × perpendicular distance from one side to center

7. Regular Polygon
   Perimeter   = sum of all sides or number of sides × one side
   Area   = sum of all sides × perpendicular distance from one side to the center, and divided by 2.

8. Circle

Circumference = $3\frac{1}{7}$ × diameter
for greater accuracy C = 3.1416 d

Area = $11\frac{1}{14}$ × diameter squared
for greater accuracy A = 0.7854 d²

Diameter = square root of the product of $1\frac{3}{11}$ × A
for greater accuracy D = $\overline{1.2732\ A}$

9. Ellipse

Area = product of the two diameters × 0.7854

10. Sphere or Globe

Area = circumference × diameter

Diameter = square root of the quotient obtained by dividing the area by 3.1416

Volume = 0.5236 × diameter cubed

11. Pyramid or Cone

Area = circumference of base × ½ slant height

Volume = area of base × ⅓ altitude

12. Frustrum of Pyramid or Cone

Area = sum of circumference at both ends × ½ slant height + area of both ends

Volume = square root of the product of the two end areas + the two end areas × ⅓ altitude.

TABLE XLVI

LINEAR MEASURE

12 inches	= 1 foot
3 feet	= 1 yard
5½ yards or 16½ feet	= 1 rod
320 rods	= 1 mile

TABLE XLVII
SURVEYOR'S LONG MEASURE

7.92	inches	=	1 link
25	links	=	1 pole
100	links	=	1 chain
10	chains	=	1 furlong
8	furlongs	=	1 mile
1	chain = 4 rods	=	22 yards

TABLE XLVIII
SQUARE MEASURE

144	square inches	=	1 square foot
9	square feet	=	1 square yard
30¼	square yards	=	1 square rod
160	square rods	=	1 acre
640	acres	=	1 square mile

TABLE XLIX
SURVEYOR'S SQUARE MEASURE

625	square links	=	1 square rod
16	square rods	=	1 square chain
10	square chains	=	1 acre
640	acres	=	1 square mile

43560 square feet = 4840 square yards = 1 acre
One acre is a parcel approximately 200 feet by 218 feet

TABLE L
CUBIC MEASURE

1728	cubic inches	=	1 cubic foot
27	cubic feet	=	1 cubic yard
128	cubic feet	=	1 cord (cd.)

0.314 cubic feet = 231 cubic inches = 1 gallon

TABLE LI
AVOIRDUPOIS WEIGHT

16	ounces	=	1 pound
100	pounds	=	1 hundredweight
2000	pounds	=	1 ton

TABLE LII
LIQUID MEASURE

4	gills	=	1 pint
2	pints	=	1 quart
4	quarts	=	1 gallon
31½	gallons	=	1 barrel
2	barrels	=	1 hogshead

1 gallon = 231 cubic inches = 0.134 cubic feet

TABLE LIII
DRY MEASURE

2	pints	=	1 quart
8	quarts	=	1 peck
4	pecks	=	1 bushel

1 bushel = 2150.42 cubic inches = 1.24 cubic feet

NOTE: The pint and the quart dry measure are about 16% larger than the pint and the quart liquid measure.

TABLE LIV
CIRCULAR MEASURE

60 seconds (")	—	1 minute (')
60 minutes	—	1 degree (°)
360 degrees	=	1 circumference

TABLE LV
MEASURE OF TIME

60 seconds	=	1 minute
60 minutes	=	1 hour
24 hours	=	1 day
7 days	=	1 week
30 days	=	1 month
365 days	=	1 year
366 days	=	1 leap year

TABLE LVI
COUNTING

12 units	= 1 dozen
12 dozen	= 1 gross
12 gross	= 1 great gross
20 articles	= 1 score

TABLE LVII
METRIC CONVERSIONS

1. Length

Centimeter	= 0.3937	inch
Meter	= 3.28	feet
Meter	= 1.09	yard
Inch	= 2.54	centimeters
Foot	= 0.305	meter
Yard	= 0.914	meter

2. Area

Square centimeter	= 0.155	square inch
Square meter	= 10.764	square feet
Square meter	= 1.196	square yards
Square inch	= .000645	square meter
Square foot	= 0.0929	square meters
Square yard	= 0.836	square meter

3. Volume

Cubic centimeter	= 0.061	cubic inch
Cubic meter	= 35.31	cubic feet
Cubic meter	= 1.308	cubic yards
Cubic inch	= 16.4	cubic centimeters
Cubic foot	= 0.028	cubic meter
Cubic yard	= 0.765	cubic meter

4. Capacity

Liter	= 0.0353	cubic foot
Liter	= 0.2642	gallon (United States)
Liter	= 61.023	cubic inches
Cubic inch	= 0.0164	liters
Cubic foot	= 28.32	liters
Gallon	= 3.785	liters

TABLE LVIII

CONVERSION OF WEIGHTS AND MEASURES

1. Length

Inch   = 0.0833   foot
Inch   = 0.02788 yard
Foot   = 0.33333 yard

2. Area

Square inch = 0.0069 square foot
Square inch = 0.0007 square yard
Square foot = 0.1111 square yard

3. Volume

Cubic inch = 0.00057 square foot
Cubic inch = 0.00002 cubic yard
Cubic foot = 0.0370   cubic yard

4. Capacity

Pint   = 0.5   quart
Pint   = 0.125 gallon
Quart = 0.25   gallon

TABLE LIX

COMMON EQUIVALENTS

Cubic foot = 7.48 U. S. gallons.
Cubic inch = .004329 U.S. gallons.
Gallon = 231 cubic inches.
Gallon = 0.134 cubic foot.
Pounds of water ÷ 62.5 = cubic feet.
Pounds of water ÷ 8.3 = gallons of water. (8.345 more accurate.)
Gallons of water × 8.3 = pounds of water. (8.345 more accurate.)
Cubic feet of water × 62.5 = pounds.

TABLE LX

SQUARES AND SQUARE ROOT

Number	Square	Sq. Root	Number	Square	Sq. Root
1	1	1.000	36	1296	6.000
2	4	1.414	37	1369	6.082
3	9	1.732	38	1444	6.164
4	16	2.000	39	1521	6.244
5	25	2.236	40	1600	6.324
6	36	2.449	41	1681	6.403
7	49	2.645	42	1764	6.480
8	64	2.828	43	1849	6.557
9	81	3.000	44	1936	6.633
10	100	3.162	45	2025	6.708
11	121	3.316	46	2116	6.782
12	144	3.464	47	2209	6.855
13	169	3.605	48	2304	6.928
14	196	3.741	49	2401	7.000
15	225	3.872	50	2500	7.071
16	256	4.000	51	2601	7.141
17	289	4.123	52	2704	7.211
18	324	4,242	53	2809	7.280
19	361	4.358	54	2916	7.348
20	400	4.472	55	3025	7.416
21	441	4.582	56	3136	7.483
22	484	4.690	57	3249	7.549
23	529	4.795	58	3364	7.615
24	576	4.898	59	3481	7.681
25	625	5.000	60	3600	7.745
26	676	5.099	61	3721	7.810
27	729	5.196	62	3844	7.874
28	784	5.291	63	3969	7.937
29	841	5.385	64	4096	8.000
30	900	5.477	65	4225	8.062
31	961	5.565	66	4356	8.124
32	1024	5.656	67	4489	8.185
33	1089	5.744	68	4624	8.366
34	1156	5.830	69	4761	8.306
35	1225	5.916	70	4900	8.246

TABLE LX
SQUARES AND SQUARE ROOT
(Continued)

Number	Square	Sq. Root	Number	Square	Sq. Root
71	5041	8.426	86	7396	9.273
72	5184	8.485	87	7509	9.327
73	5329	8.544	88	7744	9.380
74	5476	8.602	89	7921	9.433
75	5625	8.660	90	8100	9.486
76	5776	8.717	91	8281	9.539
77	5929	8.774	92	8464	9.591
78	6084	8.831	93	8649	9.643
79	6241	8.888	94	8836	9.659
80	6400	8.944	95	9025	9.746
81	6561	9.000	96	9216	9.797
82	6724	9.055	97	9409	9.848
83	6889	9.110	98	9604	9.899
84	7056	9.165	99	9801	9.949
85	7225	9.219	100	10000	10.000

CHAPTER XII

STAIR ESTIMATING*

STAIR BUILDING IS often considered as a separate occupation from house construction. Therefore, the estimating rules required to take off a bill of materials for a stairway have purposely been placed in a separate chapter. Here they can be studied more easily by, (1) the skilled journeyman carpenter or apprentice who desires to specialize in stair building; (2) the cabinet-making apprentice who is employed in a shop in which finished stairs are constructed or (3) by the apprentice stair builder.

CONSTRUCTION PROCEDURES

No one standardized procedure is followed in stair construction. *In all cases* the foreman carpenter is responsible for the actual layout work on the job, checking very closely with the blueprints and specifications in order that the framing work may be accurately done.

There are three methods followed in stair construction.

Method number one is to construct the stairway "on the job." If floor space permits, such as a large living room, and if there is a large enough opening to the stairway location, the staircase is first constructed as a complete unit and then moved into place. Sometimes the staircase is constructed in its location below the well hole but from three to four feet above the floor on which it is to rest; this permits the carpenter to work *under* the treads as they are assembled; then he drops

*See J. Douglas Wilson and S. O. Werner, *Simplified Stair Layout*, Delmar Publishers, Inc., Albany, N. Y.

the finished staircase into place when all assembly work is completed. The stair is made approximately one half-inch narrower than the distance from wall to wall and this space is covered with a base mould.

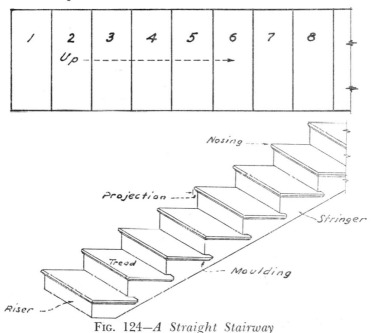

Fig. 124—*A Straight Stairway*

In every case the stair horses are constructed as a part of the framing of the house, and the finished stair is set into place on top of the rough horse.

A *second method* is to hire a stair builder and turn the job over to him. Today they are few in number and hence a splendid field of work is open to any ambitious carpentery apprentice who desires to train himself for this specialized occupation.

A *third method* that is followed is to take the job to a cabinet shop that specializes in stair work. This shop will build the complete stairway, deliver it to the job and install it.

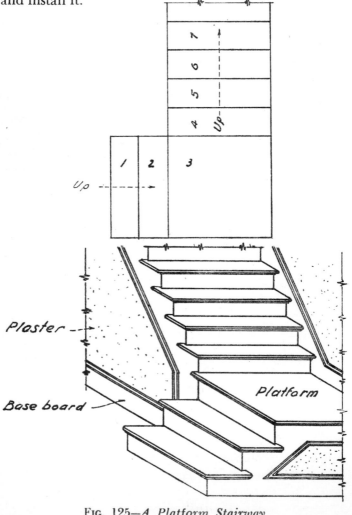

Fig. 125—*A Platform Stairway*

STAIRWAY TYPES:

For an average two-story residence the stairway will either be straight, as in figure 124, or require a platform in order to change the direction of the stairway, as in figure 125.

ESTIMATING PROCEDURES:

The estimating or take-off work for a stairway divides itself into two parts, namely the framing unit and the finish unit. The materials for each unit must be developed into a lumber list in readiness for presentation to the lumber yard or mill. The stairway framing materials are always included in the framing lumber list; the stairway finish lumber is included in the finish lumber list.

It should be emphasized that if special millwork is required, such as a detail handrail or baluster, the blueprints must be sent to the mill along with the order. It is *not* advisable to *order any finish stair materials* without taking accurate job measurements. This is quite important as well hole and stair area measurements on the job do not always conform exactly to the measurements given on the blueprint.

However, listing the materials required for a stairway can proceed in advance of any construction work as *exact* measurements are not required for a lumber estimate.

FRAMING UNIT

SAWN OR BUILT-UP STAIR HORSE: (for any stairway)

Number required: (for an average width stairway), two. Plans or specifications will indicate if more are necessary. A third or even fourth support is needed on outside stairways or for stairs in public buildings.

Thickness: For all standard framing situations 2″ is considered as sufficient thickness for a stair horse. Any requirement for a thicker stair horse would be given in the specification.

Width: For the sawn horse the width must be sufficient to make the tread rise and run triangular blocks

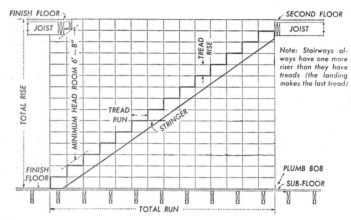

FIG. 126—*Stairway Mathematical Terms*

plus 4″ to provide a continuous support. Commercial buildings or long stairways should have 6″ of continuous material. The supporting walls and partitions under a stairway must also be considered as such supports will permit the using of a narrower stair horse.

For the built-up stair horse *two* pieces of lumber are ordered for *each* horse. The width of the piece for the triangular blocks is based on tread rise and run measurements; the width of the full length supporting member is usually 4″ or wider, the same as the width of the continuous piece on a sawn-out horse.

Length: Using the steel square, measure the diagonal of the total rise and total run, then increase to the next even foot length of lumber.

For the stair blocks one full-length piece of framing lumber will make two sets of blocks by "nesting" them when the layout work is done.

Milling: S1E to make both horses the same width.

TREADS: (or a rough or basement stairway)

Number: As shown in the blueprint.

Thickness: As specified; 2″ framing material is often used:

Width: The same as the tread run plus from ½″ to 1″ for projection.

Length: The same as the outside width of the stairway plus any projection called for, then convert to lumber lengths that will cut with the least waste.

Milling: As specified; 1″ net vertical grain Douglas Fir (or equal) is carried in stock. The trade name is "stepping." It has a half-round nosing.

RISERS: (for a rough or basement stairway)

Number: As shown in the blueprint. There is always one more riser than treads. See figure 126. On many basement stairs no risers are used.

Thickness: Usually 1″. The specifications should be consulted before listing the risers.

Width: The same as the tread rise. This may require that the riser material be ripped to a special width.

Length: The same as the outside width of the stairway plus any projection called for. Then convert to lumber lengths that will cut with the least waste.

Milling: Usually S4S stock.

NEWEL POSTS: (for a rough or basement stairway)

Made of solid framing lumber, such as 3" x 3" or 4" x 4" or 2" x 4". The stair plan will show the number required. Estimate the materials needed to make one post, then convert to lengths that will make all posts without waste.

HANDRAIL: (for a rough or basement stairway)

Number: Allow one for each side. The building ordinance should also be checked.

Thickness and Width: As detailed. Often a 2" x 3", S4S with corners rounded is used. Sometimes a piece of 2" or 2¼" round is used.

Length: As the handrail parallels the horse it is ordered the same length as the horse.

Milling: As detailed.

BALUSTERS:

Balusters are seldom used in basement stairs.

FINISH UNIT

PLAIN STRINGERS FOR A CLOSED STAIRWAY:

Number required: Two.

Thickness: Usually ¾" stock.

Width: The cut of the stairway, that is tread rise and tread run, will determine the width of the stringer board. To this must be added from 2½″ to 3″ to provide lumber above the nosing edge of the tread, to cover the plastered wall.

Length: Using the steel square, measure the diagonal of total rise and total run, then increase to the next even foot length of lumber.

Milling: S4S and sanded one side.

Kind of Lumber: As specified.

MITERED STRINGERS FOR AN OPEN STAIRWAY

Rules as given above for the closed stringer can be applied to the mitered stringer. The width will be the same although the *additional* width required is needed at the bottom edge and not the top as in the case of the plain stringer.

HOUSED STRINGERS: See figure 127

Number: On a full open stairway four stringers are required. Two of the pieces will be "housed" to receive the risers and treads; the other two will only be cut at each end and are used to cover the face of the housed stringer into which common nails have been driven and, of equal importance, to provide a suitable base for the balusters.

On a housed stairway that is constructed against a wall or partition and is, therefore, open on one side only, three stringers are sufficient as the one next to the wall is single and does not need doubling. The handrail is fastened to the wall and, of course, no balusters are needed on this side of the stairway.

Width and Length: See plain stringer above.

Milling: S4S and sanded one side.

Kind of Lumber: As specified.

TREADS

Number: As shown on the blueprint.

Thickness: As specified, 1¼" finishing lumber is often used; this will mill to 1" net.

Width: The same as the tread run plus projection. This will be at least 1"; if a cove moulding is placed

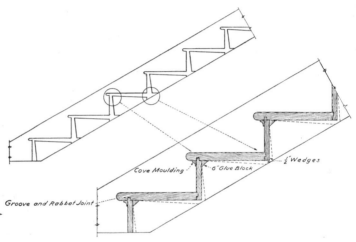

Fig. 127—*Housed Tread and Riser Construction*

under the projection 1¼" should be added. Then ⅜" must be added to allow for the lip which fits into the groove in the riser.

Length: The same as the outside width of the stairway plus any projection called for, plus 2" for cutting. Mitered stringer construction requires the tread to project *beyond* the face of the riser.

Treads are usually ordered by the piece and are not combined into long lengths of lumber.

Milling: As specified: On the housed stairway the back edge of each tread must be rabbeted to fit into a groove in the riser, the front edge must be nosed to a half-round. See figure 127.

Kind of Lumber: Finish treads are ordered made of the same kind of hardwood as the flooring. The specifications should be consulted on this point.

RISERS

Number: As shown on the blueprint; there is always one more riser than treads.

Thickness: 1″ material is standard.

Width: The same as the tread rise.

Length: The same as the outside width of the stairway plus 2″ allowance for cutting. Finish risers are usually ordered by the piece and not combined into long lengths of lumber.

Milling: Usually S4S stock sanded 1 side and grooved to receive the tread.

Kind of Lumber: As specified; front stairways usually require hardwood risers.

NEWEL POSTS: See figure 128

Number: As detailed. No set rule can be given. Closed stairways require none. Some open stairways require newel posts at every turn and also at the bottom and top ends. Occasionally a stairway will have a continuous handrail. In that case no newel posts are required. Curved pieces of handrail called easements, goosenecks, quarter and half turns are used in place of the newel posts.

Size: This varies with the detail. Sometimes the post is built up into a square shape. Special corner joints

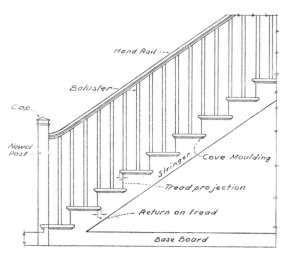

Fig. 128—*Parts of a Finished Stairway.*

are required and the job ordinarily becomes one for the cabinet shop and mill.

If the newel post is to be built up on the job then determine the thickness and width of each piece (four are required to make one post) and convert to lumber widths and lengths that will cut with the least waste. Hardwood materials are usually ordered by the piece giving the correct size plus enough in width and length to give sufficient stock to work on. Hardwood is not plentiful, hence economical methods must be followed when ordering this kind of lumber.

Length: As detailed, this will vary according to the type of handrail or the ornamental top of the post. At least 8″ should be added to the length of the first or bottom newel post to permit it to be framed into the first floor joists to secure rigidity. Second-story newel posts should be increased in length the width of the second floor joists plus at least 6″ more (depending on the detail) to give material to form a finish at the lower end of the post which projects below the ceiling line. The building ordinance should be checked for required height of the handrail as this measurement affects the length of the newel post.

Milling: As detailed.

Kind of Lumber: As detailed.

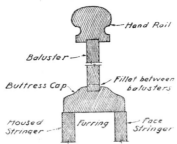

FIG. 129—*Parts of a Balustrade*

HANDRAIL: See figure 129

Number: As detailed and according to the building ordinance. The handrail may be a single piece of milled lumber fastened to the wall with handrail brackets or it may be constructed as the top member of a balustrade.

Size: As detailed.

Length: The handrail is ordered the same length as the stair stringer as it parallels this part of the stairway.

Milling: As detailed.

Kind of Lumber: As specified.

BALUSTERS: See figures 128, 130

Number: These can be counted on the detailed drawing. Plans usually show a full-size cross section of a tread and how many balusters are needed for each tread. Therefore, *number per tread times the number of treads* will give the number of balusters for the stair railing. The well hole balustrade will require additional balusters. (See below.)

Size: As detailed; turned balusters are often used. Consult the blueprint.

Length: Should be carefully *measured* on the detail sheet. Building ordinance should also be checked for height of handrail.

Milling: As detailed.

Kind of Lumber: As specified.

BUTTRESS CAP: See figure 130

This item is only required on an open stairway using housed stringers. The buttress cap is placed on the top edge of the stringers. (The housed and plain stringers are fastened face to face with furring between to give extra thickness to receive the cap.)

Number: Allow two pieces for a stairway which is open both sides. One only is required for the open stairway which is constructed against a wall.

Size: Usually a stock item carried by most mills. The details should be consulted.

Length: The same as the stringer length on which the buttress cap rests.

Milling: As detailed.

Kind of Lumber: As specified.

FILLET: See figures 129, 130

This material is ordered by linear feet as it cuts into very short pieces to fill the space in the buttress cap between each baluster.

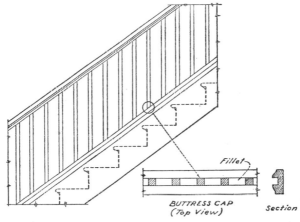

BUTTRESS CAP
(Top View)

Fillet

Section

FIG. 130—*Buttress Cap Construction*

Size: As detailed. Must fit into the buttress cap.

Length: Measure the stringer length; deduct the combined width of all the balusters that are required over the stringer; result equals linear feet of fillet required.

Milling: As detailed.

Kind of Lumber: As specified.

WELL HOLE FINISH: See figure 126

The well hole requires an apron to provide a finish over the face of the floor joists that form the well hole and a piece of nosing to cover the ends of the hardwood flooring. This nosing must be rabbeted to conform to the thickness of the hardwood floor. Also a balustrade must be constructed around the well hole to form a guard.

Quantity, Thickness, Width, and Length: Well hole finish material varies with each stairway. No rule can be given other than to consult the stair details; measure the well hole dimensions and then order lumber or milled parts that will cut with the least waste.

The rules given above for the buttress cap, fillet and balusters can be applied to the well hole balustrade.

Well hole nosing is sometimes carried in stock; it is $3\frac{1}{2}''$ wide and rabbeted to fit $\frac{1}{2}''$ hardwood flooring. The front edge is nosed to a half-round.

Milling: As detailed.

Kind of Lumber: As specified.

MOULDING: See figure 124

Moulding is often required under the tread projection. Its primary use is for architectural purposes; however; its use permits a wider projection thus increasing the width of the tread. On a stairway which is crowded for horizontal run an increase in the width of the stair tread is very much worth while.

Number: Allow one piece for each tread.

Size: Usually a stock cove moulding $\frac{3}{4}''$ x $\frac{3}{4}''$.

Length: The inside width of the stairway is the exact length of each piece of moulding. Determine number required and convert to lengths of moulding that will cut with least waste.

Milling: As detailed.

Kind of Lumber: As specified.

CHAPTER XIII

HOW TO PLAN A HOUSE

THE PROBLEMS involved in *planning* a house do not, primarily, belong in the field of estimating. However, it is a great advantage if an estimator has an intelligent understanding of the procedures which take place *before* any building is actually done. This information is, of course, a necessity for any residential building contractor. Lumber dealers, likewise find such information valuable.

The following material has, therefore, been included in the text to provide condensed reliable statements pertaining to financing, selection of technical services, how to plan a house, contract documents and budget items.

"SO YOUR GOING TO BUILD"*

HERE'S HOW

The desire to own a home is inherent in everyone. The realization of this desire is one of the most enjoyable of all experiences.

In what district should the lot be purchased—which way should the house face—how large should this or that room be—where should Junior's room be placed—these and nu-

*A booklet with this title was published by the Los Angeles Chamber of Commerce. It was compiled by members of the construction industry who were well acquainted with all construction details. Permission to incorporate the material in this text has been granted by the publishers and is hereby acknowledged with appreciation by the authors.

merous other questions constantly arise during the preliminary planning period.

Too, the all-important question of financing must be considered. How much money should one invest in relation to the neighborhood—how much should one invest in relation to his salary—these questions also require careful thought and planning. A house may represent the largest investment you will ever make.

To assist the prospective owner to intelligently plan his new house, this booklet outlines a number of items which must be considered before the house is built. It states in simple language how to determine the amount of money to invest, how to estimate financing costs, how to select a competent architect, how to select a reliable contractor.

A careful reading of these pages will add much to your pleasure of house planning. And the romance of actually seeing the building take form (always a fascinating process to the competent builder and craftsman) will become your own happy experience through an intelligent understanding of the whole procedure.

YOUR BUDGET

In a construction loan the yardstick used by most lending institutions is this:

"Monthly payments including principal, interest and taxes, should not exceed 20%, or at the outside 25%, of the applicant's monthly income."

1. *What your budget should cover*:

    a. Cost of the lot.

    b. Cost of plans, specifications and supervision.

    c. Financing cost of the house.

    d. The general contract for constructing the building.

    e. Allowance for hardware and electrical fixtures.
       (Be sure this is adequate.)

    f. Interior furnishings.

    g. Water service to the lot.

    h. Improvement of the grounds.

    i. Moving costs.

2. *Factors to be considered*:

    a. How much to invest.

    b. The relation of investment to salary.

    c. The relation of lot cost to house cost.

    e. Shape and size of the house as they may affect the
       budget.

    f. Hillside lots may require additional construction costs.

    g. Adequate neighborhood storm drain facilities.

NOTE: The above items are explained in more detail in the
following pages.

HOW TO FINANCE YOUR HOUSE

1. *Where building loans can be obtained*:

    There are a number of reliable lending institutions
from which one can obtain a building loan. These are
banks, savings and building & loan associations, Federal
savings and loan associations, insurance companies,
private mortagage companies and other reputable private
sources. The monthly payment plan, discussed later is
the most generally accepted method of financing; with
it you make payments similar to rent.

The Federal Housing Administration (FHA)* does not make loans but insures loans made through certain lending institutions.

2. *Making the loan*:

In considering a loan application, particularly in the case of an FHA insured loan, the appraiser must see that certain definite requirements are met.

For example, the contemplated improvement must be appropriate for the neighborhood.

The potential earning capacity of the borrower for the duration of the loan must be considered. For instance, in the case of an elderly couple making an FHA loan application, it is often necessary for a son or young wage-earning member of the family to act as co-signer.

Many other factors are carefully considered. If all of these are favorable, it is possible to obtain a loan up to 95% of the FHA value of the house and lot on an owner-occupied single family residence where the maximum loan does not exceed $6,000; or a loan up to 90% of the first $7,000 and 80% of an amount in excess of $7,000 up to an FHA valuation of $11,000 for a maximum loan of $9,500. Loans in cases where the FHA valuation exceeds $11,000 are limited to 80% of the valuation.

In actual practice, it is not safe to count on this maximum limit, due to the many factors affecting cost and value which must be considered by the appraisers.

Before signing your building contract or commencing construction, be sure you have definite arrangements for your financing.

3. *The initial loan expense*:

Certain necessary charges are incident to the making of any kind of construction loan. These include a loan

*The regulations governing this Federal agency may occasionally be changed. Therefore the local F.H.A. office should be consulted for the latest information. Above data is as of January, 1950.

or escrow fee, certificates of title, prepaid fire insurance (usually for three years), cost of drawing, acknowledging and recording the necessary papers and tax searches.

Including all the above charges, the average advance deposit on a typical $6,500 loan is approximately $150.00.

In addition, on a FHA loan, a deposit or impound must be made covering the *pro rata* taxes for the elapsed portion of the tax year and also for the earned portion of the fire insurance premium so that the monthly payments from then on will accumulate enough money to pay the taxes and fire insurance premium when they become due. Also, some lending institutions charge a brokerage fee which they justify on the grounds that they make a more liberal loan. With FHA loans, such brokerage charges are limited to 1% on existing construction and 2½% on proposed construction loans.

4. *Monthly cost of loans*:

In figuring the cost of monthly payments on an FHA loan, it is necessary to estimate taxes and fire insurance costs. These vary in different locations and from year to year, hence the following figures are only approximate.

Cost of monthly payment on a 25-year FHA loan including amortization of principal, interest, mortagage, insurance premium, taxes and insurance, will run from $7.80 to $8.50 per $1,000 per month. On a 20-year FHA loan the cost is from $8.75 to $9.50 per $1000 per month.

Careful consideration should be given to the rate of interest and amortization period on your loan.

HOW TO SELECT TECHNICAL SERVICES

1. *Adequate plans are needed*:

To insure complete satisfaction and protection when constructing a house it is essential that adequate plans and specifications be prepared. These plans must be approved before the loan is made. Lending institutions are able, through expert service, to estimate the approximate cost of the house and determine how large a loan it will support.

2. *How plans are prepared*:

Plans may be prepared in the following ways, but must conform to definite building requirements and ordinances.

a. An architect draws the complete plans and specifications and supervises construction for a stipulated fee, usually a percentage of the cost of the building.

b. Some contractors provide these services to their clients through their own design departments, or through their affiliations.

3. *Reliability of architect or contractor*:

The following steps may be taken to determine the reliability of the architect or contractor.

a. Check with three recent clients and inspect their buildings;

b. Check with the State Architectural Board* (on architect);

c. Check with the State Contractor's License Board* (on contractors);

d. Check bank references;

e. Find out if the contractor has had experience under the conditions to be met in your particular job.

f. Consult with your lending institutions as to the advisability of securing a surety bond.

HOW TO PLAN YOUR HOUSE

If you have secured reliable technical services, the following points will probably be brought to your attention by

*These Boards may vary in name and activity in the several States.

your technical adviser. In any event, be sure you give all points the consideration they deserve:

A. *The lot*:

    1. *Location*:

        a. Accessibility to:
            Schools
            Stores.
            Churches.
        b. Accessibility to transportation facilities.
        c. Cost of transportation.
        d. Accessibility of recreational facilities.
        e. Traffic on street.
        f. Deed restrictions.
        g. Zoning.
        h. Types of surrounding buildings.
        i. Neighborhood drainage.

    2. *Any street improvements in or contemplated?*

    3. *Are utility services available?*

        a. Water.
        b. Gas.
        c. Electricity.
        d. Sewer or cesspool.
        e. Storm drains.

    4. *The land itself*:

        a. Size and shape.
        b. Hillside or level.
        c. Drainage.
        d. Corner or inside.
        e. View.
        f. Type of soil.
        g. Filled ground.

B. *The house*:

1. *Family requirements*:
    a. Number in family? Adults, boys and girls.
    b. Study facilities for children.
    c. Closet space.
    d. Possibility of future additions to house.

2. *Architectural requirements*:
    a. Style desired.
    b. Conformity of style to neighborhood.
    c. Available sun exposures.
    d. Wind exposure or direction of prevailing winds.
    e. The view.
    f. Service yard.
    g. Accessibility of house to garage.
    h. Limited budget as it affects shape of house.
        (Few angles; minimum hall space.)
    i. Wall space requirements:
        Furniture
        Refrigerator
        Kitchen range
        Laundry equipment.

3. *General requirements*:
    a. Adequate mechanical systems such as plumbing, heating and electrical.
    b. Sufficient convenience outlets.
    c. Cabinets.
    d. Waterproofing.

e. Insulation.

f. Weather stripping.

g. Built-in accessories.

Mail box, medicine cabinets, book cases, shoe racks, door grilles, milk bottle holders, iron receptacles, garbage disposal, etc.

h. Telephone location.

i. Mirrors.

j. Awnings.

4. *Decorative features*:

a. Lighting fixtures.

b. Hardware fixtures.

c. Color schemes.

d. Wall paper.

e. Painting.

5. *Furnishings*:

a. Shades.

b. Blinds.

c. Draperies.

d. Floor coverings.

C. *Improvements of the grounds*:

1. *Construction*:

a. Walks and drives.

b. Retaining walls.

c. Steps.

d. Fences.

e. Incinerator.

f. Yard lights.

2. *Piping*:

   a. Yard water lines.
   b. Hydrants.
   c. Lawn sprinkler system.
   d. Water pressure regulators.

3. *Grading*:

   a. Drainage.
   b. Landscaping.

4. *Planting*:

   a. Lawn.
   b. Shrubs.
   c. Trees.

CONTRACT DOCUMENTS AND REQUIREMENTS

1. *Contract Documents*:

   a. The deed to the lot.
   b. Mortgage papers.
   c. The building contract (this should state approximate completion date).
   d. The plans and specifications.
   e. Fire insurance coverage.
   f. Methods of payment:

      (1) Progress payments through lending agency.
      (2) On cash job, the owner may pay the contractor progress payments up to 80% of the work in place, and should retain 20% until 35 days after notice of completion has been recorded.
      (3) Escrows.
      (4) Joint control.

2. *Legal requirements**

   a. Lien laws.

   b. Building and zoning laws and ordinances.

   c. Building restrictions (deed or tract restrictions).

   d. Compensation insurance.

   e. Notice of completion.

   f. Owner's liability insurance.

PROTECTION SERVICES PROVIDED

1. *Building ordinances*:

Building ordinances are written and passed by governmental bodies concerned with fire, health and safe construction. These ordinances state *mininmum* requirements for materials, structural design and workmanship.

These minimum requirements must be met by all contractors. Work can be held up or removed if these requirements are not fulfilled. Zoning ordinances govern setbacks, yard sizes, side yard widths, etc.

It is greatly to the advantage of home owners and in their best interests that:

   a. Sufficient light and air space be provided.

   b. The foundation, walls, floors and roof be of sufficient strength.

   c. The plumbing equipment be sanitary.

   d. The electrical installations be safe.

   e. The heating and ventilating and refrigeration equipment be safe against danger of fire, explosion and asphyxiation.

*Legal requirements pertaining to building vary between the States and between cities within the same State according to the building code and building laws in force. Building departments of the city or district in which a building is to be constructed should therefore be consulted for detailed information on the topics listed above.

Detailed information on building ordinances and special zoning matters can be secured at your City Hall.*

2. *Inspectors*:

Who are they and what do they do?

Building inspector: Control of the requirements for building safety, and plumbing, electrical and heating safety, is carried on through inspectors whose duty is to see that the minimum rules for materials and good work are met, to protect the owner, get for him a safe and sanitary house and be helpful at all times. The inspectors know what is required for a safe home; they visit the buildings to assist in carrying out the building code requirements.

Loan Inspector: It is their principal interest to see that the building is substantially completed and will afford good protection for the monies loaned. It is not their duty to inspect as the owner's representative, and they protect the lender's interests only.

Distinction should be made between complete architectural supervision and compliance inspections made by loan inspectors.

3. *Things you (the owner) should do*:

Read your specifications carefully before signing general contract. The specifications are an important part of your contract as they specify just what materials and workmanship are covered by your contract.

Acquaint yourself with the quality of materials specified; the manner in which they will be installed; the types of fixtures; the number of coats of paint. Changes after the building is started may entail additional ex-

*The location of inspection and building departments is based on the organization plan of the local community government and may not always be in the City Hall.

pense. *You are entitled only to the items that are specified.*

Building ordinances and lending institutions have certain minimum requirements, but many items such as painting, fixtures and finish are strictly up to you.

You also owe it to yourself to become acquainted with what the market affords. There are many building exhibits and show rooms where practically everything that goes into a building can be seen and studied.

The Budget Items listed below should be carefully checked. Every item to be included must be either a part of your general contract or included elsewhere in your budget.

Be sure a completion date is specified in your contract. Check on your allowances for items such as hardware and fixtures. Are they adequate? What do they include?

If additions or changes are necessary after the work has been started, be sure you issue signed orders for the work.

BUDGET ITEMS

Prospective home owners should check carefully and account for each item listed below in order to be sure that everything required or desired is actually included, either in some contract agreement or provided for in their separate budgets.

Check	Items	Where Included	Budget Amount
The Lot:			
☐	a. Purchase Price	. . . .	$ . . . .
☐	b. Dealer's Commission	. . . .	. . . .
☐	c. Unpaid Taxes	. . . .	. . . .
☐	d. Unpaid Assessments or Bonds	. . . .	. . . .

Check	Items	Where Included	Budget Amount
☐	e. Title Search	. . . .	. . . .
☐	f. Title Insurance	. . . .	. . . .
☐	g. Escrow Costs	. . . .	. . . .
☐	h. Legal Fees	. . . .	. . . .
☐	i. Lot Survey	. . . .	. . . .

The House and Improvements:

☐	a. House Cost	. . . .	. . . .
☐	b. Garage Cost	. . . .	. . . .
☐	c. Architectural Fees	. . . .	. . . .
☐	d. Permit Fees	. . . .	. . . .
☐	e. Contractor's Bond	. . . .	. . . .
☐	f. Lighting Fixtures	. . . .	. . . .
☐	g. Hardware	. . . .	. . . .
☐	h. Linoleum	. . . .	. . . .
☐	i. Blinds and Shades	. . . .	. . . .
☐	j. Cesspool	. . . .	. . . .
☐	k. Window Cleaning	. . . .	. . . .
☐	l. Moving Costs	. . . .	. . . .
☐	m. Water Service Fee	. . . .	. . . .

The Grounds:

☐	a. Walks and Drives	. . . .	. . . .
☐	b. Sprinklers (lawn)	. . . .	. . . .
☐	c. Yard Water Lines	. . . .	. . . .
☐	d. Grading and Drainage	. . . .	. . . .
☐	e. Lawns, Shrubs, Trees	. . . .	. . . .
☐	f. Retaining Walls	. . . .	. . . .
☐	g. Fences	. . . .	. . . .
☐	h. Incinerator	. . . .	. . . .

Financing:

☐	a. Appraisal Fees	. . . .	. . . .
☐	b. Legal Fees	. . . .	. . . .

Check	Items	Where Included	Budget Amount
☐	c. Advance Taxes	. . . .	. . . .
☐	d. Service Charges	. . . .	. . . .
☐	e. Mortagage Insurance	. . . .	. . . .
☐	f. Title Fees	. . . .	. . . .
☐	g. Advance Interest	. . . .	. . . .
☐	h. Fire Insurance	. . . .	. . . .

Total Budget Requirements:

$. . . . .

Finally:

Remember the suggestions contained herein—*plan carefully*—and building a house will be one of the most thrilling and satisfying experiences in your life.

INDEX

A

Abbreviations, 11
Adjustable shelf hardware, 142
Adjusters, sash, 133
Apron, 119
Architect, selection of, 269
  responsibilities of, 145
Area rules, 239
  ceiling, 242
  floors, 241
    building with take-away area, 242
    circular building, 241
    rectangular building, 241
    square building, 241
  gables,
    combination shed and gable, 247
    gable roof, 247, 248
    gambrel roof, 247
    shed roof, 247
  partitions, 239
  roofs, flat, 243
    gable, 243, 246
    gambrel, 244
    hip, 244
    intersecting, 245, 246
    shed, 243
  walls, building, 240
    firewall, 241
    room, 240
    straight, 240
Area tables, door and window, 166
  roof, 61
Avoirdupois weight table, 258

B

Backing, ceiling, 57
  wall, 50
Balance, sash, 131
Balloon framing, 51
  ribbon for, 51
  studs for, 51
Balusters, 271, 275, 276

Baseboard, basemould and shoe, 119
Baseboard plaster grounds for, 55
Basic information for hardwood, 129
Bead, parting, 87
Belt course, 94
Blind stops, 86
Blocks, concrete, 27
  pier, 30
Blueprint, fractional measurements on, 9
Boards, corner, 94
  form, 15
Board foot constant table, 157
Board foot reckoner, 254
Bolts, 18, 128
Bookcase, 216
Braces, 17, 23, 49, 72
Brick, foundations, 26
Brick unit, common, 26
Bridging, herringbone, 39
  solid, 38
Broom closet, 210
Budget, building, 280
  grounds, 281
  house, 280
  items, financing, 280
  lot, 280
Building guide, 144
Building information and tables, 144
Building material ordering information, 153
Building material purchasing units, 157
Bumper, door, 138
Buttress cap, 276
Butts, door, 137
  cabinet, 139
  front door, 135
  inside door, 137
  parliament, 132
  sash, casement, 132
  screen, window, 134

C

Cabinets, bookcase, 216
  broom, 210
  dish, 205
  dish and drawer, 208
  kitchen cabinet and cooler, 206
  kitchen sink, 203
  linen, 212
  mantel shelf, 218
  medicine, 214
Cabinet door hardware, 139
Cabinet material short cut table, 201
Cabinet unit, 122, 201
  job made, 123
  mill made, 122
  parts, 123
Carpentry labor, 226
Carpentry mensuration, 234
Casement sash hardware, 132
Casement window jambs, 82
Casings, inside, 116
  mullion, 118
  outside, 85
Catches, elbow, 141
  friction, 141
Ceiling, backing, 57
Ceiling joists, 56
Ceiling, T. & G., 96, 126
Ceiling unit, 56
  backing, 57
  joists, 56
  stiffeners, 57
Cement contractors estimating method, 25
Checking list, estimating, 222
  hardware, 151
  lumber, 147
  millwork, 150
Check up measurement sheet, 5
Check-up procedure, 12
Circular measure table, 259
Coat and hat hooks, 142
Columns, concrete, 21
Common brick unit, 26
  brick foundations, 26
  mortar, 27

Common rafter, length of, 63
  number of, 64
Composition roofing paper, 100
  roof sheathing, 70
  shingles, 100
Concrete blocks, 27
Concrete block unit, 27
  concrete block, 27
  mortar, 28
Concrete footing and wall table, 160
Concrete form unit, 13
  boards, 15
  bolts, 18
  braces, 17
  nails, 18
  oil, linseed, 19
  spreaders, 19
  stakes, 16
  studs, 16
  tie wire, 17
  whalers, 16
Concrete materials unit, 20
  cement contractor's method, 25
  construction methods, 21
  form content, 22
  foundation parts, 21
  measuring unit, 22
  sand and rock, converting, 24
  voids, allowances for, 22, 24
Concrete pier table, 161
Concrete quantities, 24
  aggregate, 25
  blocks, 28
  footings and walls, 160
  piers, 161
Constants, see Tables
Contract Documents, 288
  legal requirements, 289
Contractor, reliability of, 284
  selection of, 284
Content of form, figuring, 22
Conversion, decimal, table, 253
  metric table, 260
  parts-of-a-foot, 252
Converting sand and rock, 24
Cord, sash, 131

Corner boards, 94
Cornice, box, 97
  open, 95
Cornice, unit, 95
  box cornice, 97
  open cornice, 95
  rafter, verge, 96
  sheathing, 96
Counting table, 260
Cove brackets, 52
Cribbing plates, 31
Cribbing studs, 32
Cubic measure table, 258
Cupboard, broom, 210

D

Decimal conversion table, 253
Dish cabinet, 205
Dish and drawer cabinet, 208
Division, estimating, 2
  framing, 29
  finish, exterior, 75
    interior, 105
  foundation, 13
  hardware, 127
Doors, 112
Door and window area table, 165
Door and window stops, 115
Door frame, inside door jambs and
  door stop table, 164
Door jamb, inside, 114
  outside, 83
Door or window frame sills, 87
Double acting door hardware, 138
Double hung window hardware, 131
Drawer lumber, 199
Drawer, hardware, 141
Dry measure table, 259

E

Equal pitch roof areas, 243
Estimating, check-up sheet, 5
  checking list, 222
  divisions, 2
    finish, exterior, 75
      interior, 105
    foundation, 13
    framing, 29

  hardware, 129
  labor, carpentry, 226
  materials, 4
  preliminary steps, 3
  tables, (see Tables)
Exterior finish, 75
  cornice, 95
  frames, 75
  roofing, 98
  walls, 88

F

Face frame lumber footage table,
  220
Fasteners, sash, 133
  door, cabinet, 140
  screen, door, 136
    window, 134
Filler, 59, 73
Fillet, 277
Figuring content of form, 22
Finance your home, how to, 281-283
Finish, exterior, 75
  interior, 105
Finish hardware unit, 128
  drawer, 141
  door cabinet, 139
  double acting, 138
    front, 135
    inside, 137
    screen, 136
  hooks, coats and hat, 142
  information, basic, 129
  lumber short cut table, 184-220
  sash, casement, 132
  screen, window, 134
  shelf, adjustable, 142
  window, double hung, 131
Firestops, 48
Firewall sheathing, 54
Fixtures, shelf, 142
Floor and roof areas, mathematical
  relationship between, 60
Floor joists, 35
Floor, sub, 40
Floor unit, (framing), 35
  bridging, herringbone, 39
    solid, 38

building paper, 43
joists, floor, 35
  header, 37
  sub-floor, 40
Flooring pine, 125
  hardware table, 125
Flooring unit (interior) 124
  hardwood, 124
  pine, 125
Form boards, 15
Form, figuring content of, 22
Form studs, 16
Form unit, concrete, 13
Foundation
  brick, 26
concrete, 21
  concrete blocks, 27
  construction, 21
  forms, concrete, 14
  parts, 21
Fractional measurements on blue-
    print, 9
Frames, job made, 81
  mill made, 75
Frames, window and door, 76
  table, 164
Frame unit, 75
  job made, 81
    bead, parting, 87
    casings, outside, 85
    jambs, door, outside, 83
      window, casement, 82
    moulding, plaster, 86
    sills, 87
    stile, pulley, 84
    stops, blind, 86
  mill made, 75
  window and door frames, 76
Framing, balloon, 51
  information, general, 43
  short cut lumber table, 177-183
  Western, 46
Frieze, 59
Fundamentals, estimating, 1

G

Gable areas, equal pitch roof, 247
  unequal pitch, 248
Gable studs, 72

General framing information, 43
Girders, 34
Glass, window, table, 107
Glue blocks, 272
Grounds, improvement of, 287
  construction, 287
  grading, 288
  piping, 288
  planting, 288
Grounds, plaster, 55
Guide, building, 144

H

Handrail, 270, 275
Hanger, screen, 134
Hardware, 127
  adjustable shelf, 142
  cabinet door, 139
  casement sash, 132
  checking list table, 151
  coat and hat hooks, 142
  double acting door, 138
  double hung window, 131
  front door, 135
  inside door, 137
  screen door, 136
  unit, (see Finish hardware)
  window screen, 134
Hardwood flooring, 124
Header hoists, 37
Headers, top, 49
Headroom, 268
Hinges, screen door adjustable, 136
  cabinet, 139
  double acting, 138
  ornamental, 140
  screen door, 136
Hip roof, 182
Hip or valley rafters for equal
    pitch roof, length of, 64
  for unequal pitch roof, length
    of, 66
  number of, 68
Hooks, coat and hat, 142
Hookstrips, 120
Horses, stair, 73, 267
House, architectural requirements,
    286
  decorative features, 287

family requirements, 286
furnishings, 287
general requirements, 286
How to finance your house, 281-283
How to plan your house, 284-288
How to select technical services, 283
Hypotenuse lengths, braces, 236
    herringbone bridging, 236
    rafters, common, gable roof, 238
        shed roof, 237
        hip, 238
    stair horse, 239

I

Indications, plan, 9
Inside door hardware, 137
Inside casings, 116
Inside door jamb table, 164
Inside trim unit, 113
    apron, 119
    baseboard, 119
    baseshoe, 119
    casings, inside, 116
    hookstrip, 120
    jambs, door, 114
    moulding, picture, 120
    threshold, 121
    stool, 118
    stops, door, 115
        window, 115
Interior finish, 105

J

Jamb, door inside, table, 164
    outside door, 83
Job made cabinets, 123
    frames, 81
Joists, ceiling, 56
    floor, 35
    header, 37

K

Kinds of rafters, 62
Kitchen cabinet and cooler, 206
Kitchen sink, 203
Knobs, door, 140
    drawer, 141

L

Labor, carpentry, table, 228

Labor hours per unit of work, 226
Length of, common rafter, 63
    hip or valley rafter for equal
        pitch roof, 64
    for unequal pitch roof, 66
Lifts, sash, 132
    screen, 134
Linear measure table, 257
Linen closet, 212
Linseed oil, 19
Liquid measure table, 259
Loans, building, 281
Locks, door, front, 135
    single acting, 137
    drawer, 141
    sash, 132
Lot, evaluation of, 281
    land itself, 285
    location of, 285
    utility services, 285
Lumber checking list, 147
    estimating short cuts, 177
    how to determine ordering unit, 6
    reckoner, 254

M

Mantel shelf, 218
Materials, foundation, 13
    to be estimated, 4
Material unit, concrete, 20
Mathematical relationship between
    floor and roof areas, 60
Measurement check-up sheet, 4
Measure of time, 259
Measure, unit of, for concrete, 22
Medicine cabinet, 214
Mensuration, table, 256
    circle, 257
    cone, 257
    ellipse, 257
    frustrum of cone, 257
    globe, 257
    hexagon, 256
    parallelogram, 256
    pyramid, 257
    rectangle, 256
    regular polygon, 256
    sphere, 257
    square, 256

trapezoid, 256
triangle, 256
Metric conversion table, area, 260
    capacity, 260
    length, 260
    volume, 260
Mill made cabinets, 122
    frames, 75
Millwork checking list, 150
Mirrors, 108
Mortar table, brick, 27
    concrete blocks, 28
Moulding, cornice, 98
    picture, 120
    plaster, 86

N

Nails, 127
    concrete form, 18
    quantities, (table), 175
    sizes, (table), 174
Newel posts, 270, 273
Number of common rafter, 64
    hip or valley rafters, 68
    jack rafters, 68

O

Oil, linseed, 19
Open cornice, 95
Ordering information for building
    materials, 153
Ordering unit for lumber, how to
    determine, 6
Outside casings, 85
Outside door jambs, 83
Owner responsibilities, 145, 290

P

Paper, building, 43, 55
    composition roofing, 100
Parting, bead, 87
Partition areas, 239
Parts, foundation, 21
Parts of a cabinet, 123
Perimeter rules, 234
    buildings with offset corners, 235
    building with wall off-set, 236

circular, 235
    rectangular, 235
    square, 235
Perimeter table, 159
Picture moulding, 120
Pier blocks, 30
Pine flooring, 125
Pitch, what is, 60
Plan abbreviations, 11
    indications, 9
    specifications, 10
    symbols, 9
Plaster grounds, 55
    moulding, 86
Plates, bottom, 46
    cribbing, 31
    push, 139
    top, 46
Posts, newel, 270, 273
    roof, 73
    underpinning, 33
Preliminary steps when estimating,
    3
Protection services provided, 289
    building ordinances, 289
    inspections, 290
Pulls, drawer, 141
Pulley, sash, 131
    stile, 84
Purline, 73

R

Rafter, kind of, 62
    length of, common, 63
        hip or valley, 64, 66
    number of, common, 64
        hips or valleys, 68
        jack rafters, 68
    summary of, 69
    verge, 96
Rests, shelf, 142
Ribbon for Balloon framing, 51
Ridge, roof, 71
Risers, stair, 269, 273
Rock, concrete, 24
Roof area rules, summary of, 71
Roof areas, equal pitch, flat, 243
    shed, 243
    gable, 181, 243

gambrel, 244
hip, 244
intersecting, 245
unequal pitch, gable roof, 245
    plates same height, 245
    plates not same height, 246
Roof sheathing, composition, 70
Roofs, types of, 60
Roof unit, 58
braces, 72
filler, 59, 73
pitch, 60
rafters, kinds of, 62
length of common, 63
length of hip or valley, 64, 66
number of common rafters, 64
    hips, 68
    jacks, 68
    valley, 68
ridge, 71
roofs, types of, 60
rules, area, 60, 71
sheathing, composition, 70
    shingle, 71
studs, gable, 72
summary of length rules, 69
Roofing, slate, 102
Roofing unit, 98
paper, composition roofing, 100
shingles, composition, 100
    wood, 98
    slate, 102
Rough hardware unit, 127
bolts, 128
nails, 127

S

Sand and rock, converting to tons
    or cubic yards, 24
Sash pulleys, 131
Sash weight table, 173
Screen door hardware, 136
Screens, window, 108
Sets, interior door, 137
Sheathing
    cornice, 96
    firewall, 54
    roof, 70

shingles, 54
storm, 53
tongue and groove, 96
Shelf hardware, adjustable, 142
Shingles, composition, 100
    wood, 91, 98
Shoe, base, 119
Short cuts, estimating, 177
cabinet materials, 201
    bookcase, 216
    broom closet, 210
    dish cabinet, 205
    dish and drawer cabinet, 208
    kitchen cabinet, 203
    kitchen cabinet and cooler, 206
    linen closet, 212
    mantel shelf, 218
    medicine cabinet, 214
finish lumber, 184
frames, double hung and case-
        ment sash, 184
    exterior door, 187
framing, 177
    ceiling unit, 180
    entire frame, 182
    floor unit, 178
    roof unit, 180
    underpinning unit, 178
    wall unit, 179
inside trim, 190
    doors, exterior, 190
        inside, 195
    drawers, 198
    window frames, 192
Shrinkage due to voids, allowance
    for, 24
Shutters, 111
Siding, 88
    table, 90
Sill, door and window, 87
    foundation, 30
Sink cabinet, 203
Slate, roofing table, 102
Spacing table, 32
Specifications, 10
Spreaders, 19
Square measure table, 258
Square and square root table, 262

Stair construction, 264
Stair estimating, 264
Stair horse, 73
    unit, 73
Stair materials, finish, 270
    framing, 267
Stairway, platform, 266
    straight, 265
Stakes, form, 16
Stiffeners, 57
Stile, pulley, 84
Stool, 118
Stops, blind, 86
    door and window, 115, 164
Stringer, housed, 271, 272
    mitered, 271
    plain, 270
Studs, cribbing, 32
    for Balloon framing, 51
    form, 16
    gable, 72
Sub-floor, 40
Summary of rafter length rules, 69
Surveyor's long measure, 258
    square measure, 258
Symbols, plan, 9

T

Tables,
    areas, door and window, 166
        roof, 61
    avoirdupois weight, 258
    board foot constants, 158
    brick, common, 26
    bridging, 39
    building guide, 145
        materials, 153
        purchase units, 157
    cabinet materials short cuts, 201
    circular measure, 259
    common equivalents, 261
    concrete quantities, 24
        aggregate, 25
        blocks, 28
        footings and walls, 160
        piers, 161

conversions, decimals, 253
    metric, 260
    weights and measures, 261
counting, 260
cubic measure, 258
decimal conversion, 253
door frames, 164
dry measure, 259
estimating short cuts, 177
    cabinet materials, 201
    finish lumber, 184
    frames, 184
    framing lumber, 177
    inside trim, 190
estimator's checking list, 222
face frame lumber shortage, 220
finish lumber short cuts, 184
flooring, hardwood, 125
frames, door, 164
    window, 163
framing lumber short cuts, 177
glass, window, 107
hardware checking list, 152
jambs, door, inside, 164
labor, carpentry, 228
linear measure, 257
liquid measure, 259
lumber checking list, 148
lumber reckoner, 254
measure of time, 259
mensuration, 256
metric conversion, 260
millwork checking list, 150
mortar, brick, 27
nails, quantities, 175
    sizes of, 174
parts-of-a-foot, 252
perimeter, room, 159
rafter lengths, common, 61
    hip and valley, 65
sash weights, 173
sheathing, solid, 70
    wood shingles, 55
shingles, composition, 101
    wood, 92
shortcuts, estimating, 177
siding, 90
slate roofing, 102

spacing, 32
square measure, 258
squares and square root, 262
stops, door, 164
sub-floor, 42
surveyor's long measure, 258
  square measure, 258
weights, sash, 173
window frames, 163
wire sizes and weights, 17
T & G ceiling for wall and ceiling, 126
Technical services, how to select, 283
Threshold, 121
Tie wire, 17
Top and bottom plates, 46
Top headers, 49
Total rise of a stairway, 268
Total run of a stairway, 268
Tread projection, 274
Treads, stair, 269, 272
Trusses, 72
Turns, cupboard, 140
Types of roofs, 60

U

Underpinning unit, 29
  blocks, pier, 30
  braces, 34
  girders, 34
  plates, cribbing, 31
  posts, 33
  sill, 30
  studs, cribbing, 32
Unequal pitch roof areas, 245
Unit of measure for concrete, 22
Units, estimating, 2
  cabinets, 122, 201
  ceiling (framing), 56, 180
  common bricks, 26
  concrete blocks, 27
    forms, 13
    materials, 20
  cornice, 95
  finish hardware, 128
  floors, framing, 35, 178
  flooring, interior, 124
  frames, 75, 184

inside trim, 113, 190
roofs, 58, 180
roofing, 98
rough hardware, 127
stairs, framing, 73
underpinning, 29
walls, exterior finish for, 88
  framing for, 43, 179
windows, sash, doors and shutters, 105

V

Verge rafters, 96
Voids, allowances for, 22
Volume rules, 249
  basement walls, 250
  concrete forms, 250
  excavating, basements, 249
    trenches, 249

W

Walls, basement, 23
Wall backing, 50
Wall sheathing for shingles, 54
Wall unit, exterior finish, 88
  belt course, 94
  corner boards, 94
  shingles, 91
  siding, 88
  water table, 93
Wall unit, framing, 43
  backing, 50
  balloon, 51
  braces, 49
  brackets, cove, 52
  firestops, 48, 52
  grounds, 55
  headers, top, 49
  information, general, 43
  plates, bottom, 46
    top, 46
  ribbon, 51
  sheathing, firewall, 54
    shingle, 54
    storm, 53
  studs, 47, 51
  western, 46

Water table, 93
Wedges, stair, 272
Weights, sash, table, 173
Well hole, stair, 277
Western framing, 46
Whalers, 16
Window and door frames, 76
Window area table, 165
Window frame table, 163
Window jambs, casement, 82
Window, sash, door and shutter
    unit, 105
  doors, 112

screens, window, 108
shutters, 111
windows and sash, 105
Window screens, 108
Window screen hardware, 134
Window sills, 87
Wire, tie, sizes and weight tables, 17
Wood shingles, 98
Wood shingle sheathing, 71

Y

Your budget, 280
Your house, how to plan, 284

NOTES

NOTES

NOTES

NOTES

NOTES